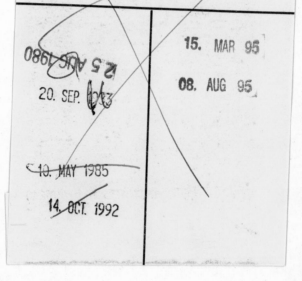

THE WOOD AND THE TREES

THE WOOD
AND THE TREES

A Biography of Augustine Henry

SHEILA PIM

MACDONALD : LONDON

First published in 1966 by
Macdonald & Co. (Publishers) Ltd.,
Gulf House, 2 Portman Street, London, W.1
Made and printed in Great Britain by
Purnell & Sons, Ltd.,
Paulton (Somerset) and London.

PREFACE

On a sunny summer afternoon in 1957 a ceremony was held in the National Botanic Gardens, Dublin. It was the unveiling of a plaque in honour of the late Alice Henry in the Augustine Henry Forestry Herbarium. I had known Mrs. Henry slightly. I knew her husband's memory was revered by all my more knowledgeable gardening friends. I had not known till then that Augustine Henry had been one of the really great plant collectors, or that he had also been a great pioneer of forestry.

As I then occasionally contributed articles on gardening to the *Irish Times*, I wrote one for the occasion and was invited to the unveiling. It was a gathering of quiet, distinguished, mostly elderly people interspersed with younger relations and ex-pupils of Professor Henry. I was impressed by the affection and esteem that everyone there felt for both the Henrys. In that lovely place, at that highly civilised party, their memories were so very much alive.

Many people said that Augustine Henry's life ought to be written. I asked for permission to look at the material available. I found there was far more to write about than plant collecting. There was, indeed, far more than enough for one book. I hope gardeners will forgive me for putting in more about people than plants. I hope foresters will forgive me for glancing only superficially at their so complex science. I should like to have said far more about Alice Henry, who was charming. But the book has taken shape of itself. It insisted on being written. I hope the pleasure I have had in doing it may be communicated to the reader.

I want especially to thank the relations of both the Henrys for their patience with me and their very kind hospitality and help: Dr. Peter Kerley for the loan of a notebook which has been the key to many sources of information; Brigadier Crum for the loan of *Notes on the Economic Botany of China* by Henry, and other help; Mrs. Campbell, Dr. Brian Henry and Miss Marie Kerley, for the information they supplied. To Mrs. Henry's sister, Mrs. Kruming, I am greatly indebted for her untiring help in looking up family letters, photographs, and papers, for writing her own recollections, and for allowing me to quote from her diary. Mrs. James Smith kindly supplied notes on the life of her great-aunt, Alice Stopford Green.

No biography could have been attempted without access to the unique series of letters written by Henry over many years to Miss Evelyn Gleeson, and I cannot be sufficiently grateful to her nieces, the Misses Katherine and Grace MacCormack, for allowing me to keep these in my own hands so long. They also lent me a photograph.

Dr. T. J. Walsh, Director of the National Botanic Gardens, Dublin, gave me most useful introductions and advice and allowed me to study Henry's own copy of *The Trees of Great Britain and Ireland* with correspondence interleaved and annotations in Henry's writing. I also have to thank him for permission to reproduce the Henry portrait, to photograph the table given by Elwes to the Henrys, which is now Dr. Walsh's, and to take photographs in the Botanic Gardens.

The Director of the Arnold Arboretum at Harvard provided me with copies of a large number of letters written to Professor Sargent by Henry on both botanical and personal matters. These had to be typed out by two members of his staff, Miss Carroll and Miss Sutton, to whom I wish to express my thanks. The Director of the Royal Botanic Gardens, Kew, kindly allowed me to make extracts from the important material there, and I wish also to thank the Librarian, Mr. R. Desmond, who searched the files for me. Others whom I have to thank for the use of manuscripts are: the Trustees of the National Library of Ireland, the Director of the Shelton Abbey School of Forestry, and Mr. Connlagh Legge of the Chicago Natural History Museum.

The Director of the New York Botanic Gardens, and Professor M. V. Laurie of the Commonwealth Forestry Institute,

Oxford, supplied me with information about work on hybrid trees.

For answering miscellaneous queries I must thank the Directors and staff of the Smithsonian Institution and the Library of Congress, Washington, and the Massachusetts Institute of Technology, the Librarians of the Linnean Society of London and the Royal Anthropological Institute of Great Britain and Ireland; Mr. S. G. Harrison, Keeper of the Department of Botany in the National Museum of Wales; the Keeper of Oriental Manuscripts in the British Museum; the Director of the Academy of Science, Peking; the Deputy Keeper of the Public Record Office, Belfast; and the Parish Priests of Cookstown, County Tyrone, and Greenlough, County Antrim.

Miss Walpole of Mount Usher, Co. Wicklow kindly helped me to identify a number of Henry's plants growing there. Mr. H. M. Fitzpatrick most patiently answered many enquiries on forestry matters. Mr. C. S. Kilpatrick very kindly helped me to obtain local information in Northern Ireland, and informed me of forestry developments there. Thanks are also due to Mr. O. V. Mooney.

In connection with illustrations, as well as those already mentioned, acknowledgment must be made to the Department of Lands, Forestry Division, Ireland, and particularly to Mr. T. O'Carroll and Mr. A. M. S. Hanan; also to Miss Findlater and to the Director of the Royal Botanic Gardens, Kew.

The lines at the end of Chapter 5 from the poem *Endurance* by A. E. are quoted by permission of Mr. Diarmuid Russell.

Numerous other people have gone out of their way to help me with introductions, recollections, references and visits. I have thanked them personally but should like here to list them in alphabetical order: Mr. Rewi Alley, Mr. N. V. Brasnett, Mr. Buttress, Mr. Padraic Colum, Mr. John Conan, Mr. E. H. M. Cox, Miss Janet Dunbar, Miss Fannin, Mrs. Fry, Professor Gorman, Mr. Miles Hadfield, Mr. H. A. Hyde, Mr. G. Jeffares, Miss Jane B. Killips, Dr. H. Martin Leake, Mr. G. H. McLean, Colonel R. B. Molesworth, Miss Elsie Patton, Mrs. Lennox Robinson, Miss Roche, Mr. James Simpson, Mr. Stelfox, Mr. R. S. Twigg, Professor D. A. Webb and Mr. G. R. G. Worcester.

Finally I must warmly thank my friend Mr. Desmond Clarke, Librarian of the Royal Dublin Society, for help and advice of every kind, and his Assistant, Mr. Alan R. Eager, for discovering much recondite material, and both of them for their sympathetic interest in the book.

SHEILA PIM.

Old Bawn

CONTENTS

LIST OF PLATES

INTRODUCTION

In May, 1885, there arrived at Kew a packet of seeds from I-chang in the middle of China with a request for identification. The sender was a doctor in the Imperial Chinese Customs Service. He went on to say:

"A good number of medicines are grown about here and there seems to be a fair number of interesting plants, and as this part of China is not very well known to botanists (at any rate as compared with the south and also the northern and maritime provinces) interesting specimens might be obtained. I know very little of botany and have scarcely any books of reference. However, I should be glad to collect specimens and forward them, if you think they would prove useful. In this case any hints would be acceptable. Trusting I have not trespassed too much on your valuable time and on your patience, I am, yours obediently,
Augustine Henry,
M.A., L.R.C.P. (*Ed*)."[1]

This diffident letter, remarkable, as it turned out, for its understatement, marks the beginning of a new epoch in gardening.

It marked, also, a turning point in the life of the writer. Augustine Henry, who was twenty-eight that year, was a clever young man bogged down in a dull job far from home. He had come to China four years earlier, partly because as a Roman Catholic of modest parentage he had few prospects in Ireland where he was born; partly, perhaps, because he had been mildly crossed in love; but mainly because of an inborn love of wandering, and a lively curiosity that ruled him all his life. By now he had shed his illusions. I-chang, a port on the

Yangtze-kiang, a thousand miles from the sea at a point where an intractable mountain barrier ends the plain, was a place where the glamour of the east soon wore off.

The Customs post was there because it was the head of steam navigation on the Yangtze. The town had a Chinese population of about 30,000 but the foreign community was limited to Customs and consular officials and a few missionaries. Adventurous characters occasionally passed through, going on into western China to spread the gospel, shoot big game, collect plants or develop markets, but nobody who could help it stayed there long.

"Life here is very monotonous," Henry wrote to a friend at home. "I am sorry to say there is not even a tiger. I envy Jim his shooting powers. I have got various armaments, but I am a wretched shot, which is curious, as I play tennis very well and have not a crooked eye, and my hands are steady, but perhaps I am a 'butter fingers'. . . . Though we are bereft of ladies' society here—I lately exported the two missionary ladies that were here homewards and now we have none—we get on pretty well. The country is charming, but I cannot get much away. I am now studying botany a little."[2]

He was writing to the sister of the Jim mentioned in the letter. They were friends of his student days. This family, the Gleesons, had been the centre of a lively circle in Galway, and at their home, Benown House, near Athlone. They had introduced Henry to the arts. "Do you remember," says his letter, "the supper we had out at Salthill and the gentleman who warbled on the flute?" But all that was far away. Evelyn was studying painting in London, another sister was a singer. Jim was in the Indian Civil Service. He later volunteered for service on the Burmese frontier, where he was killed by Dacoits.

Thousands of lives were squandered in the long slow process of infiltration of the East by the West. China was falling a prey to pioneers of the new empires, the British, the French, the Germans, the Russians and the Americans were all there for what they could get. Earlier in the century the British had gone to war with her to defend their trade, which was principally in opium. They had secured Hong-Kong as a colony and the opening to foreigners of several new ports. Nowadays the approach was peaceful penetration. The diplomatists of the powers kept whittling away at anti-foreign regulations. They struck hard bargains with the Manchu dynasty in return for getting it out of its financial difficulties. They wangled their way into spheres of influence, secured "most-favoured-nation" clauses and extra-territorial rights. Their consular officials, traders, ship-owners, railway engineers, even their scientists and missionaries, were spying out the riches of the land. The western powers were confident of dividing China among themselves whenever the old order should collapse.

The staff of the Imperial Maritime Customs were in a different category from other foreigners. The origins of the Service are interesting, as another side to the picture. In the 1850s the Chinese had risen in rebellion against the Manchu emperors and there was a time of general chaos. The rebels took Shanghai, and the Chinese Customs officials there quit work. But the consuls of Britain, France and the U.S.A., who were established by then in the treaty port, collected the taxes due from their nationals and paid them to the imperial government. They also paid them in full, without deducting the customary Chinese percentage or "squeeze". When order was restored (with foreign help), the government wanted this arrangement to continue. The French and Americans, however, got out of it and the British were left doing the job. In the end it was decided that the consuls concerned should resign from the British service and be employed by the Chinese. The Customs was reorganised, and became a tremendous asset to China, under the able direction of an Ulsterman, Sir Robert Hart.

Officials like Henry, therefore, were working in China's own interests. But this did not make them any less alien. Wherever they were stationed they automatically formed part of the foreign colony. They tended to have the worst of both worlds. Their allegiance to the Chinese made them somewhat suspect to other westerners, while their western outlook remained unreconciled to the methods of the East.

"I have seen so much that I positively hate to see a Chinese mandarin, he is such a mass of dishonour in spite of his polished ways and smooth words. It is difficult to get at their way of thinking, because we associate intellect and good manners with honesty and good conduct. . . .

"It is only the poor and uneducated in these countries who are honest and deserving. Their learned are pedantic brutes, hypocritical scoundrels."[3]

"Here in the Orient, no one cares for truth, though lying and deceit are not by any means so common as is thought. But truth is not worshipped as a special virtue. The atmosphere of slipshodness, inaccuracy, etc., is most tiring and wearisome."[4]

So wrote Henry at intervals during the fifteen years more that he remained in China. He was wearying of it already at I-chang. Those westerners who escaped war and disease often went quietly mad. Among the small groups in isolated places there were usually some drug addicts and neurotics. Henry was one who managed to keep his balance. He had the courage necessary for making the best of a situation. He was interested in his fellow humans and could get on with the oddest. But he had the traditional Irish temperament, combining gay good humour and social talents with a capacity for agonies of introspection. Often he thought of his life as wasted, and the future indeed looked blank. He had nothing to look forward to but years in outposts and retirement on a small pension. Most people at some stage in their lives feel lost in the wood, like Dante. Many a time in China, and even in after years, it looked to Henry as if he would never get out. Yet, unknown to himself, he had, at I-chang, already found his path.

If Augustine Henry's name is remembered now, it is chiefly by knowledgeable gardeners. Occasionally it is mentioned in between-the-seasons articles on "the story behind the labels", though not as often as those of E. H. Wilson, George Forrest, Reginald Farrer and F. Kingdon-Ward. He was the forerunner of all these great collectors. It was he who opened up the vast wild flora of China. Not the plants already grown by the Chinese in gardens, the roses, paeonies, chrysanthemums, camellias, azaleas and primulas created by selection and crossing over the centuries. Those had already furnished eighteenth-century walled gardens and Victorian conservatories. Collectors had also covered, as Henry said in his first letter, the flora of the maritime provinces, which included many clematises, kerrias, jasmines, deutzias and other garden treasures. No one thought there could be much more to find. Yet the flowers of these regions where farming had been done intensively through the ages were not even a sample of the riches of the natural vegetation that survived intact in hard remote places, in the wild inaccessible mountains that had always been closed to foreigners, and soon were to be so again. Kingdon-Ward said in a broadcast in 1955: "We can count ourselves fortunate that in the first half of the present century British plant hunters explored the highest and most difficult mountain ranges of the east." Light was thrown on many botanical problems, and gardeners were supplied with plants in astronomical numbers. Not till botanists alight on some new planet can anything like this happen again.

Yet Henry himself was no gardener. He never even thought of himself as a genuine botanist. Botany for him was a hobby he took up to keep himself sane in the immense boredom of exile. Out of his spare time pursuit he developed a love of trees which led him, when he got out of China, to make forestry his career. It was then a comparatively new science. He did much to advance it and became a leading expert of his day. But he was no narrow specialist. All his life he was torn between the work he had chosen (which he attacked and pursued with tremendous thoroughness), and the wider interests always tempting him off the beaten track. This is a very common problem. The interest of Henry's life is that he lived in so many worlds and touched life at so many points, as well as making his own not inconsiderable contribution. It is the story of a man for whom the world was full of a number of things, and who got a great deal done in spite of it.

2

The story begins and ends in Ireland and even when it wanders farthest Irish history is bound up in it. For Henry was Irish through and through. It was his inescapable heritage. The years that China consumed, the friends and opportunities that England gave him in full measure, never obliterated his sense of where he belonged. It happened that the years in which he at last began to find himself (he was a slow developer) coincided with that renaissance of hope and spirit at the turn of the century when to be Irish became an exciting thing. In fact the desire to "do something for Ireland" was his main reason for taking up forestry. Ireland, however, did not exactly jump at him. It was ten years more before, having made his reputation, he was offered a chair in the College of Science in Dublin. For him it meant relegating himself to a backwater, but he never hesitated. He went back on the eve of the first world war.

The world, of which Henry was by then very much a citizen, appeared to be disintegrating, and what happened in Ireland looked like the end of all his hopes and dreams. He had no sympathy with violence, yet some of his closest friends were movers in the events that led up to the rebellion of 1916. These included the Anglo-Irish aunt of his second wife, whom he had married in London, and whose brother was killed in France that same year. Those were terrible years for people with friends in every camp.

Through the "troubles" Henry went steadily on with lecturing and research. Fortitude suited him better than heroics. It was not the first time it had been required of him. From China, during the Boxer rising, when expecting his Customs post to be attacked, he had written to Evelyn Gleeson: "All day we have been busy with monthly and quarterly reports, etc., etc., and if by any chance we were suddenly to be transformed into angels, our books will be found up to date."[5]

So when peace came he was able to help on the development of Ireland's natural resources, and also to win his country good-will abroad, for in his last years his expert knowledge was consulted by foresters all over the world. He received honours from many countries. He died in 1930. It was not a bad time to go. He could have felt that he was leaving the world better than he found it.

Henry might have cut a grander figure and left more of a legend but for the simplicity of his character. A friend has called him "a simple soul". He was not altogether that. But he had a horror of pretentiousness, and though he liked to be liked he was serenely indifferent to appearances. Someone enquiring for him asked, "How is Henry? Is his tie still up over his collar?"[6] From manhood to old age he wore plain steel-rimmed glasses and a soup-strainer moustache. People began by enjoying him as a character, and progressed to holding him in high esteem. E. H. Wilson wrote from the backwoods of Sze-Chwan that he was welcomed by the inhabitants of every little hamlet where Henry had been.[7] H. J. Elwes, his friend and patron, a formidable personage, when visiting Formosa, met a French resident of Henry's time there, fifteen years before. "Know Henry!" this gentleman exclaimed, and flung his arms round Elwes's neck and kissed him on both cheeks.[8]

Compared with the empire-builders, the gunmen, the orators and agitators of the period, Henry offers a biographer only an anti-hero. Yet he is an attractive subject. He reminds one of George Herbert's lines:

> "Only the sweet and virtuous soul
> Like seasoned timber, never gives."

As a forester, he might be pleased with the comparison.

List of Sources and References relating to
numbers inserted in text begins on page 221.

PART ONE

The White Man's Burden

I

What Henry knew of his origins is sketched by his widow in a notebook that she compiled for her husband's nephew, Dr. Kerley. The record reflects, not so much family pride, as the desire of right-thinking people in the days of the Gaelic revival to link themselves up with the most ancient tradition. The Henrys were the O'Annerigh, or O'Innerigh, a ruling family of Ulster. The name means "shepherd". They were a fair, brown-haired people who may have come from France (ethnography was one of Augustine's side-lines). They are mentioned in the Annals of the Four Masters as having, about A.D. 1000, presented a bell to the great church of Derry.

The O'Innerigh had land in East Derry near Draperstown. They were dispossessed at the time of James I's Ulster plantation, and their property was handed over to the London company of the Drapers. This plantation was a reprisal for the rebellion of Hugh O'Neill and Red Hugh O'Donnell, last of the great Irish chieftains, who fled the country after their defeat. Most of the confiscated land was occupied by Scottish Presbyterians who never became assimilated. A sporting and farming people, all tribally connected in a complex of love-hate relationships, found themselves up against rootless go-getting outsiders who had come to stay. The newcomers have since struck roots, but there are still two different breeds in Ulster. The difference is modern Ireland's principal irritant. It flared up in Henry's lifetime with the Ulster Protestants' resistance to Home Rule. It crystallised in the fixing of the Boundary, which still remains. Yet in his boyhood the north-south problem was only latent. Ireland was then all one country, governed by Big Brother from another island.

Leaving the O'Innerigh in the mists of dispersal we come to the Henrys. According to the notebook, from about 1650 onwards there were Henrys living some thirty miles from Draperstown at Tyanee, near Portglenone, County Antrim. The name is very common there to-day. They were Roman Catholics, and through the years of the Penal Laws they could only earn their livings in small ways close to the land, but the lot of the small farmer was better in Ulster than other provinces. Tenants had an interest in their holdings and some protection against eviction. Augustine Henry's grandfather had built a farmhouse at Tyanee.

Augustine's father, Bernard Henry, was one of the two hundred thousand who emigrated in 1847, the year of the great famine. He went to America, was in the Californian gold rush in 1849, and went on to the Australian gold fields. He came home without having made any fortune, and when visiting a married sister in Scotland, met there and married a Miss Mary MacNamee. MacNamee, says the notebook, was the name of the former bards of O'Innerigh, so Augustine was descended on both sides from the same ancient Irish clan.

Bernard Henry went into the flax business, as some kind of middleman, buying flax from farmers and selling it to manufacturers. Flax was then grown all over east County Antrim; now it is almost all imported. He had a house in Cookstown, but also spent a good deal of time at Tyanee and sent the children there in the summers. Augustine was the eldest child. There were two more boys and three girls. Then Mrs. Bernard Henry died, and her place with the children was taken by their grandmother Henry.

Despite the early loss of his mother, Augustine's boyhood was very happy. The Henrys were a united family. Though widely scattered in later life they kept in touch, and no ups or downs of fortune cancelled the family ties. They had a strict Roman Catholic upbringing and most of them remained devout. Augustine lapsed. Reason and faith were at odds in the late nineteenth century everywhere. He was the intellectual of the family, and his great hero was Darwin. Yet he was strongly influenced by the religious teaching of his early years. The agnosticism he professed was another matter from the shallow atheism of a man who does not know what religion is about. He held the Church in respect, though he might criticise the workings of some of its institutions, such as Chinese missions.

His conduct was grounded on Christian principles. It seemed to him that they worked.

He often referred ruefully to his having been named after a saint, and said his life story should be called "The Confessions of Sinner Augustine". Saintly or not, the name seems to have struck his brothers and sisters as cissy, and they called him "Austin", the usual abbreviation in Ireland. He only became Augustine as part of the sad process of growing up.

He was born in 1857, ten years after the great famine which killed off hundreds of thousands. Very little was happening then in Ireland. People were thankful to be alive and too much stunned to rebel. There were the beginnings of secret societies. Irish emigrants in America were determined to change the old order at whatever cost. But violence seldom broke out and was soon put down, and so far there was little talk of reform by other methods. The Home Rule Party was founded only in 1870 when Austin Henry was thirteen. And whatever resistance there might be to English rule, there was none to anglicisation. The old Irish fairy tales and ballads were despised and the old language no longer spoken.

In some ways country life was idyllic:

"I remember so many things that sound so out-of-the-world now. The quiet pastoral life of the people in the glens of Antrim, where I spent two or three summers at a very pretty place on the sea. An old Irish-speaking lady who lavished once on me all the terms of endearment of the Celtic language; I wonder if they still speak Irish in Tyrone. My first day in Dublin, where I was so pleased with the politeness of the people—but I could go on for ever."[9]

Grace and civility, not as a veneer but as the fine flowering of simple decency, were virtues he became acquainted with in childhood and prized highly all his life.

But there was another side to it:

"To me, brought up in the north of Ireland, where savage bigotry prevailed, especially in my youth, it is easy to understand how anti-foreign feeling exists in China, and at times bursts forth in demoniacal ways. Europeans represent to the Chinese non-religion, and coupled with it they fear for their country."[10]

It was not only bigotry that showed him the darker side of

pastoral virtues. Drink was a great evil. It was a symptom of low morale.

"I often think of some of the poor people who lived in the country near the farm where I used to spend the summer as a boy. How good and kind and gentle and loving and graceful they were, some of them; in the depths of poverty, in utter misery, they were courageous, honest, pure, modest. Do such people live anywhere else? I suppose they do. It is so easy for people with money to be good and have nice virtues. That those poor people made so light of their poverty was perhaps a fault; it kept back the race in the world struggle. Still I like to think of them. When I was a boy I did little else, when not reading, but look into people, how they lived and thought. I used to wonder at the brutes of men who were so coarse with their drink and so on; the others so knavishly cunning; others so cruel and impatient with their children—I thought it exceedingly stupid. Afterwards I understood how it was so easy to be a child, so hard to be a grown-up."[11]

He went to Cookstown Academy, the principal local school; it has been absorbed into Cookstown High School. There he made friends with a singular person, a man of twenty, a carpenter, who had taught himself to read and write, and who entered the school as an ordinary pupil and won his way by a scholarship to Queen's University. He was the first working-class man to enter Queen's. His name was James Mullen. He wore a red muffler and wrote humorous verse. He and young Austin Henry had long talks. His example fired the boy to teach himself Latin and go to college.

Queen's University consisted of three colleges at Cork, Galway and Belfast. They had been founded in 1850 to provide higher education on undenominational lines, and though intended by the British government as a gesture towards Roman Catholics they were regarded by many as simply godless. They had also the drawbacks of being raw and provincial which made it hard to attract the best men to their chairs.

"I never really look back on my college days with *approval*, except as regards the friends I made and the women whom I knew. I always had a contempt for most of the methods used in teaching: and knew perfectly well that I was putting up with a second-rate sort of thing. I believe, however, Belfast is much improved. Of course one can't have the antiquity or the associations manufactured"—he was thinking of Cambridge, where he had stayed as guest of a don—"but a good live institution, if modern, is no ineffectual substitute." (Redbrick universities take heart!) "The Queen's Colleges were not much alive, in many ways. The truth is that the *men* at the head of them were poor creatures for the most part. I did approve of some, e.g., Prof. Clelland at Galway was a *man*, one to do splendid work for any place. I must not forget, however, that the Queen's Colleges turned out many excellent men— out of their students. My complaint lay in the Professors, who were not enough in earnest."[12]

Such as they were, they provided a gathering ground for lively minds, not bounded by the Ascendancy outlook of Trinity, Dublin, nor by strict dedication to Catholicism like Maynooth. The students were a representative cross-section of the brightest young men in Ireland, outside its ruling class. If the teaching was poor, it stimulated their critical faculties. They educated each other.

The Gleesons, already mentioned, were the centre of Henry's social life in these days. Their father was a doctor who had given up practice and founded the Athlone Woollen Mills. Their house, Benown, was on the Shannon. There were festive gatherings there in Christmas and summer vacations, winter skating, summer picnics. (Nobody, however, as yet played lawn tennis, which soon became the mainstay of middle-class amusement. It had only just been codified under Wimbledon rules, and it was a far cry from there to Galway. Henry learnt to play in Shanghai.)

Another of the crowd was Joe Fisher. He was another kind of young man, a Belfast Protestant, and indeed in himself almost an epitome of the other Ulster. Later he was a founder member of the Ulster Liberal Unionist Association, and editor of *The Northern Whig*. He was also the northern representative on the three-man Boundary Commission of 1924. He was a solid, self-confident person, subject to teasing about his figure and his opinions. But this friendship, too, survived.

The women Henry knew played a considerable part in his education. They were not, of course, fellow students. It was

before the days of university education for girls. Evelyn Gleeson got her brother's friends to coach her in their subjects. She
was a shy, gifted, serious-minded girl, two years older than
Henry. He always looked on her as a mentor, and the early
bond between them was strengthened when he married a friend
of hers, his first wife, who died early. They maintained a pen-
friendship through his years in China, and since she was one to
whom he could write what he really thought and felt, his letters
to her paint a self-portrait, invaluable for his biography.

Austin was very much of a ladies' man. He was himself
endowed with feminine sensibility, and sympathised with
women as an oppressed minority. There was a normal amount
of flirtation in the Gleeson circle, and he was credited with his
share of old flames, but he was no philanderer. He was an
out-and-out romantic, cherishing the most chivalrous ideals,
and he did not escape heartbreak. There was a mysterious
Miss Weir "who found me a cub and taught me much".[13] And
there was Miss Watters, to whom he proposed, and who rejected him without exactly explaining why.

She was the daughter of the Presbyterian Minister at Newtownards. Henry had gone on from Galway to Queen's
College, Belfast, had become friendly with her brother, Frank,
and was a frequent visitor to the Manse. Her daughter writes:
"She herself told me she could not bring herself to say to him
that it was impossible for her even to consider a Roman
Catholic, and he was certain that she preferred her two other
suitors at the time . . . because they were the sons of rich men!
As my mother never had the slightest idea of the value of
money this had its ironic side. A. H. gave her the hard-brown-
covered copy of George Eliot's *Middlemarch* which I still possess.
She loved and treasured it."[14] She married one of the other
two suitors, a divinity student.

Henry must have paid for most of his own education, by dint
of winning various grants. He took examinations in his stride.
His main idea at this time seems to have been to prolong his
student days, and he took up medicine not so much from a
sense of vocation as because it was a condition attached to a
studentship.

He learnt very young to manage money so as not to be
obsessed by it. To him it was common sense to live within

one's means. "I have always saved money myself (of course
I spent it afterwards) by a very simple plan, i.e., by not buying
anything except what was absolutely necessary. Even at
college from 1874 onward I always lived within my income. I
only mention this, not as self praise, but to show that it is
possible to cut one's coat according to the cloth. It is very
vexatious to be pressed for money and it cuts away one's
independence."[15] His idea was to "curtail unnecessary expenses and so have more freedom to spend a little money on
charitable objects and personal whims". It was not too hard at
college in Ireland, where there was never any shame in being
impecunious, but he applied the same rules successfully in
more affluent society.

In 1877 he took his B.A. degree at Galway with first-class
honours and a gold medal. The following year he graduated
M.A. of Queen's College, Belfast. He then spent a year at a
London hospital, and in 1879 passed the Queen's University
examination in medicine. It was then that he became fired
with the idea of going to China.

The Watters family may have had something to do with this.
There was a brother seventeen years older than Henry's
friend, who was in the British Consular Service. He became
an authority on Confucius and Lao-Tzu. He also did some
plant hunting and he and Henry met later in the East. At
one time he came back home bringing with him a Chinese
manservant in blue and white native dress and with a pigtail,
which he tucked inside his clothes in Newtownards. This could
have been Henry's first encounter with a member of the race
he was to know so well.

It also chanced that in 1878 Sir Robert Hart came back to
Europe, to preside over the Chinese commission at a great
Paris Exhibition. He was an ex-graduate of Queen's, and he
took the opportunity to revisit his old university and enquire
about likely candidates for the Chinese Customs Service.
Applicants had to have medical qualifications. Henry's were
not sufficient, but when the possibility was mentioned to him
by one of the professors he decided to apply. He discovered
that he could get the degree he needed quickly at Edinburgh
by taking special examinations at double fees. He also passed
the routine examination for the Customs Service, for which

he had to have a working knowledge of Chinese. After this examinational marathon he was appointed to a post at £420 a year, and set out for China in the summer of 1881.

As he wrote to Evelyn Gleeson, "One must philosophize and not be such a goose as expect to dissipate always."

2

Henry landed first in the British colony of Hong-Kong. He called on the Chief Judge, who was a Queen's University man, and who introduced him to the Chief Manager of the Hong-Kong and Shanghai Bank, who had been a clerk in the Bank of Ireland in Armagh. In a day or two he got orders to report at Shanghai and went on there in a small coasting steamer. His first introduction to China proper was the mud of the Yangtze-kiang, discolouring the sea a hundred miles from the great river's mouth.

In later years Henry came to loathe Shanghai. At first acquaintance it seemed quite a jolly place, though very hot. One slept under a punkah. It was pulled by a coolie who slept too; he had trained himself to keep it moving. All night the air was dead still. From six to ten in the morning it grew steadily hotter as the sun rose in the sky, then usually a breeze blew up and relieved the heat. Office hours were from ten to four with an hour off for lunch. Before lunch and dinner all the men from the consulates and banks and business houses congregated in the Shanghai Club. The chief amusements were racing and tennis. In the evening a good band played in a park reserved for foreigners on the river bank. People lay in long chairs and listened under the stars.

Henry used to get up at five or six and ride outside the Settlement for an hour or two, returning for breakfast and a bath. Early rising was always a habit with him. He liked to have time to himself before the working day. Much of his plant collecting was done in these morning hours.

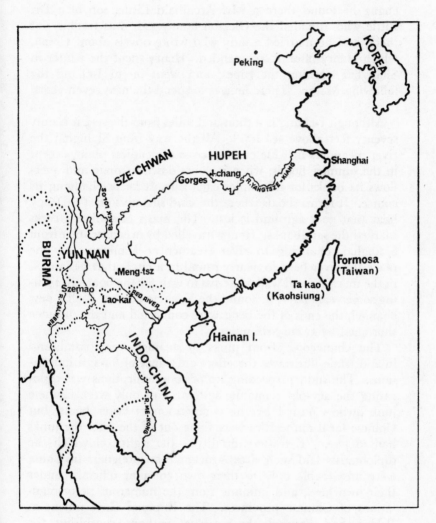

Augustine Henry's Stations in China

He found plenty of Irish in Shanghai. The British Consul-General came from Newry, and he was befriended by a leading doctor who came from Cork. Even when he went on to I-chang he found there a Mr. Archibald Little, son of a Dr. Little who attended the Gleeson family. He was trading out there, and he married a lady who wrote novels about China, which Henry often recommended. Henry spent the winter in Shanghai learning the ropes, and went on to I-chang the following March. There he was to spend the next seven years.

Although I-chang is a thousand miles from the sea, it is only seventy feet above sea level. All the way from Shanghai the river meanders in wide curves across the endless plain, except in the summer floods, when it pours down in spate and over-flows its banks for fifty miles each side. It keeps changing its course. It forms shoals where the sand silts up so fast that any boat that goes aground is lost. The masts of sunken wrecks marked the sandbanks. Henry travelled by ocean steamer from Shanghai, changing to river steamer at Hankow. At one place the river bent so nearly round in a circle that he landed in the morning and walked across to wait for the boat. Return-ing some years later, he found the Yangtze had cut itself a new channel, the ends of the bend were connected and the distance shortened by twenty-six miles.

The changeover from junks to steamers for coastal and inland trade illustrates the effect on China of foreign innova-tions. The sudden speeding up of communications was dislo-cating the age-old economic system. Not only were Chinese junk owners ousted by the competition of faster boats, but Chinese local authorities were done out of the dues the junks had to pay. "Extra-territoriality"—the rights on which the diplomatists laid such stress—meant that foreigners in China were answerable only to their own consular officials, under their own laws, and immune from the numerous petty regu-lations of Chinese provinces. The Imperial Government at Peking had granted these rights, without consulting the administrators of the provinces. Sir Robert Hart disapproved of them. As he wrote, "Extra-territoriality may have relieved the native official of some troublesome duties but has ever a disintegrating effect, leading the people on one hand to despise their own government and officials and on the other to envy and dislike the foreigner withdrawn from native control."[17]

Each Chinese province had its own local administration, and disliked interference from Peking. The ruler of all China, then and for many years more, was, surprisingly, a woman. She was a dowager-empress, acting as regent for a child emperor. There had been two regents, two dowager-empresses, but they had disagreed and the other one had unaccountably died. The empress inhabited a palace staffed by eunuchs, who spied for her, and whose advice she tended to prefer to that of her ministers. All the western diplomatists mistrusted her, and her own subjects regarded her as a usurper. The Manchus had seized the throne from the Ming dynasty two hundred years before.

Wicked old woman as she was and a shocking contrast to Queen Victoria, she had held the Chinese empire together by sheer force of character; she had kept the Chinese a nation when by all the logic of history they should have been divided and scattered. And Sir Robert Hart respected her. Ulstermen respect efficiency. But he was also a gentleman of extreme integrity. He saw that she was doing her duty by China, and he, in his great experience of the Far East, had developed an immense sympathy for the Chinese. As for her family being usurpers, his own forebears had come to Ireland in the same century with William of Orange, and two hundred years seemed long enough to him. He was a good subject of Queen Victoria, but he was loyal to the Chinese Imperial Government. When the British wanted him to become their ambassador at Peking he declined the honour, saying that he could do more good where he was.

High politics were far outside the sphere of a Medical Officer and Assistant in the Customs at I-chang in the province of Hupeh, where Henry spent the next seven years. The daily routine was much the same as at Shanghai without the gaiety. It was uncomfortably hot in summer and miserably cold in winter, when there was usually snow and hardly ever any frost.

The surrounding country was rather dull, although the plain began at last to break up in little hills; curiously regular little hills like those in Chinese drawings. One imagines the artist has imposed symmetry on the landscape, but it may be the

c

other way round. The only trees and shrubs were those left
round temples. The Chinese cultivators cut down trees
as ruthlessly as they weeded out unprofitable plants. All over
China there was a shortage of timber, which was why furniture
was made of bamboo. Wood was one of the principal imports
along the Yangtze. Henry was impressed by this scarcity. It
was many years before he turned forester, but it was at I-chang
that he first recognised the value of trees to man.

But only four or five miles farther up the river there began
one of the most fantastically beautiful regions in the world. The
Yangtze forces its way down from the impassable mountains
and the rich mountain basin of the province of Sze-Chwan,
through a hundred miles of gorges, all limestone country, such
as can be seen at Cheddar, or in the Burren of County Clare,
but only in miniature by comparison. The Cliffs of Moher
are seven hundred feet high, the precipices of the Yangtze
Gorges reach two thousand feet. Tributaries of the great river
have cut ravines of their own. There are waterfalls pouring out
of the rock face and rumblings of underground springs, rocks
weathered into strange shapes, caves pillared with stalactites
and stalagmites. It is the landscape of Coleridge's opium dream.
Small wonder that for the inhabitants it is peopled with demons.
They have made magnificent pathetic attempts to ward them
off, by building pagodas on the most inaccessible heights, so
that human hands have actually managed to enhance the
weirdness of the natural scene.

All this extravagant landscape of rock and water teems with
life. Roses and lilies grow there in profusion. The air on
summer mornings is laden with scent. Creepers fling themselves from rock to rock, and where there seems to be no soil
at all the ledges become encrusted with saxifrages and even
primulas. "At the entrance of the I-chang Gorge," says one
of Henry's notes, "there was a stream coming in from the north
side, down a very narrow ravine, and where the ravine joined
the main river there was a temple in a cave, looked after by a
Buddhist monk. This cave was known as the 'San Yu Tung',
that is, the cave of the Three Pilgrims. On the side of the cliff
just beyond the cave there was a great display on a ledge for
a quarter of a mile or more, in winter, of the Chinese primula
of a beautiful species which lived on a ledge of pure limestone

without any soil. . . . These ledges of primula are often continuous for hundreds of feet and in December and January, when the flowers appear, present a scene of great beauty. Flowers pale lilac verging to pink."[18] The vegetation differed in each ravine. The wild life also was fascinating. An English naturalist, Antwerp Pratt, came to I-chang. He made a great collection of butterflies and discovered many new species of snakes and fishes. Henry himself shot a new kind of antelope. He sent the skin and horns to a learned zoologist in Shanghai, and it was named *Kemas Henryi*.

The Gorges led into a rich and densely populated part of China called the Red Basin. Goods destined for Chungking, the next stop, and centre for this area, were transhipped at I-chang into native boats which had to be hauled along by men on the bank. It took eight or ten men to a boat, but there were times and places where as many as two hundred men were needed, and the people who lived along the river made their living by hauling. The navigation of the Upper Yangtze was much discussed among the westerners, who saw no reason why steamboats should not make the passage. Henry's friend, Archibald Little, had a pioneer steamer some years later. His plans fell through owing to political unrest, but steam traffic came in the end. Now, of course, one can fly to Chungking.

Henry could only get to the Gorges at weekends. The rest of the time he was tied to his office. His first collecting was done in the near neighbourhood of I-chang. One of his rarest finds was a weed in a pond not far from the Customs House. It is called *Trapella sinensis*, and is of no interest to gardeners, but quite a lot to botanists. Kew has only two other examples on record, and though Henry looked for it often he never found it again.

Henry started collecting plants as part of his routine duties. Consuls and Customs officials looked on plants as raw materials. The British Foreign Office from time to time brought out reports on vegetable products. The Imperial Maritime Customs compiled returns of them as imports and exports. It was just part of the job.

The Customs at this time was taking an interest in Chinese medicines. Its local officials were requested to supply detailed lists of the plants from which were derived the drugs that

passed through the various Customs posts. Doubtless they
grumbled at the jobs thought up for them at head office. It
was no easy matter in the first place to get hold of the correct
Chinese names, and there often seemed to be no English name,
so how were you to discover the Latin one? Henry, having a
smattering of botany as part of his medical training, was the
one who got this thankless job. He found the vagueness of the
reference books exasperating. He would not tolerate in his
own work the "atmosphere of slipshodness" which prevailed in
China. Hence his first letter to Kew.

He was on the brink of a morass of muddle. Years later,
when he had gone farther in, he wrote as follows to a Customs
colleague: "The question of attacking the nomenclature in
Customs Returns is a large one. . . . One must remember the
framers of the tariff were ignorant of botany, textile fibres and
such like. Medicine includes substances that should properly
be classed as dyes. . . . Many errors are of great importance;
e.g., into Shanghai they import a so-called 'star aniseed' from
Japan which is a virulent poison. It is apparently used to
adulterate the Kwangsi and Annam true fruit. I have often
thought it might account for some of the summer cholera in
Chinese cities."[19]

The seeds he sent came from a tree used for varnish. It was
not identical with *Rhus vernicifera*, the source of Japanese
lacquer, and he never did succeed in tracking it down. The
seeds were sown, but there is no word of their having come up.
At Kew, however, they had a paper of routine instructions for
would-be collectors and they sent him a copy. In September
he wrote again.

"I have made during the past few months a collection of
plants growing in the neighbourhood and I intend sending you
a quantity of dried specimens. These plants I shall *number*,
and the help I desire of you is—if it will not be too much
trouble—that you will give me the scientific names corres-
ponding to the plants and their *numbers*." (This is characteristic of Henry, civil but firm.) "I have had a man in the
mountains collecting, but he has not done very well. You will
see that I am only beginning, but I hope to be of service to
you—and that you will also kindly aid me in acquiring some
knowledge. It is very difficult for me often to get at all near what

genus a plant may be of.''[20] (Not surprising as there were ten new genera included.)

He dried his specimens carefully between pieces of ordinary Chinese paper, under boards weighted down with books, changing the paper every day. After a few days they were dry enough to be made up in bundles, separated by single sheets. Each was labelled with particulars of the locality where it grew, native name, size and uses of the plant. Henry was meticulous over details. To avoid mistakes he took as his motto, "Label where you pick."

The sorting took longer than he expected, but his first collection, which amounted to a thousand plants, was sent off the following November. In the files at Kew there is a note on it by Oliver, then Curator of the Herbarium: "This collection is one of the most important which we have ever received from the interior of China."

Henry would have been the last man to want to steal anybody else's thunder. Some account, however sketchy, must be given of the other great men in the field. Collecting had been going on in China ever since the first foreigners got a foothold. It was a favourite side-line of old China hands, and several times professional collectors had been sent out. During the eighteen-nineties a Russian called Bretschneider published a *History of European Botanical Discoveries in China* in two big volumes. Henry only takes up a few pages, though more than most individuals. "He has given a sketch of my travels," he wrote to Evelyn Gleeson, "and it is funny to read one's biography."[21]

Robert Fortune was the first nineteenth-century collector to work outside the limits of the Treaty Ports. He was employed by the Horticultural Society, and also by the East India Company. For the latter, he went in disguise to find out how tea was cultivated, and stole some plants, which made the beginnings of the tea industry in India and Ceylon.

After his time the great Taiping rebellion of the fifties and sixties devastated twelve provinces and travel again became impossible. It was not till the eighteen-seventies that scientists began to venture into the mountains of the interior. A French priest, Father David, explored the borders of Tibet, and the

Tsinling mountains in central China. He was an all-round naturalist, not a specialist in plants. He was borrowed from the missions by the French government. Russia was the next power to become inquisitive about these regions, and expeditions were sent under the botanists Przewalski and the Potanins. These pioneers were unlucky. Father David lost some of his collections in a shipwreck, others disappeared in France through carelessness, and the rest were not sorted out for many years. The Russians also were slow in dealing with botanical specimens. There had been a great Director of the botanic gardens at St. Petersburg, Maximowicz, who encouraged exploration, but he died in 1890, and the new finds were neglected.

This is more understandable if one thinks of the labour involved. Every item in a plant collection has to be scientifically described and then compared with type specimens in order to identify it. The rarer a plant is, the longer this takes. Descriptions are circulated to all the world's great herbaria for comparison before anything can be established as new. Some of these specimens belonged to new genera, not merely new species. They could not be fitted into any of the great plant families then known to botanists. Moreover, in that age of exploration collections were coming in from all over the world. Every botanic garden had a backlog of material waiting to be examined.

The Paris Museum of Natural History was certainly overwhelmed by the material it received from Henry's contemporary, Father Delavay. He is the one collector whose achievement rivals Henry's, and the ground he covered was not dissimilar; he travelled on mission work up the Yangtze, through the Gorges and beyond Chungking as far as Sui-fu, then went overland south-west into the province of Yunnan, where Henry was stationed later on. He sent the Museum more than two hundred thousand specimens, belonging to about four thousand species. Franchet, the director, published a first short list in 1885, began a fuller catalogue in 1886, which did not get beyond the letter A, and in 1889 undertook to compile a volume of *Plantae Delavayanae*, but did not live to finish it. In the eighteen-nineties Delavay's work was known only vaguely to the initiated.

If Henry rather than Delavay was the man who revealed to

the outside world the riches of the wild flora of China, it was thanks to the remarkable co-operation he got from Kew.

During the nineteenth century Kew had built up an empire-wide botanical service, under a series of able Directors. Sir William Hooker had been succeeded by his son, Sir Joseph, and he in turn was succeeded in 1885 by his son-in-law and assistant, Thiselton-Dyer. This was the man with whom Henry had to do, and he could not have found a better person. It is no small advantage to an explorer in the field to have personal encouragement and advice from an expert at home. In later years George Forrest enjoyed a similar relationship with Sir Isaac Bayley Balfour of Edinburgh. If only Delavay could have been in closer touch with Franchet it would have been easier for them both. Botany is team-work.

The primula that grew along the ledge by the cave of the Three Pilgrims had been sent home by Delavay. For a long time it was supposed to be the wild form of the well-known cultivated *Primula sinensis*. Henry's note, which was written later in his life, continues: "Mr. Hutchinson proved clearly that the I-chang plant differs materially from *P. sinensis* and gave it the name of *Primula calciphila* (lover of limestone). This primula has been described and figured in the Botanical Magazine Tab. 8986. The cultivated *P. sinensis* appears to be a more southerly plant, coming from the S. of China, introduced in 1821 by Captain Reeves. The I-chang primula was sent home as seed by Wilson in 1906 and the plate in the Bot. Mag. was prepared from a batch of plants raised by Miss Willmott."[22] So much for the care taken in identification, and so many botanists go to one plant!

3

The mysterious plants that the Chinese used for drugs did not all grow round I-chang. Many of them were from the mountains. Henry questioned the peasants who came in from the country and got one or two of them to collect for him. It soon dawned on him that there must be more in the mountains than had ever yet come to the knowledge of botanists.

His employment of Chinese helpers was itself an innovation. A few native collectors were trained at the botanic gardens at Hong-Kong, but the officials in outposts did not place much reliance on the local people, or had not the patience to instruct them.

Three years before Henry arrived in I-chang a professional collector had been sent there by Veitch's nurseries. He only stayed a week and reported that there was nothing worth while. It is fair to say that he was collecting conifers, and he was still a long way from the forests, yet how could a man turn back who had once glimpsed the glories of the Yangtze Gorges? He must have had some kind of trouble with the Chinese, for he lost his luggage. He was evidently reluctant to return.

Henry never stirred up trouble. He had a gift for getting on with people of every caste and colour. Perhaps it was that to him everyone was a fellow human being. It was not a case of them and us, he met people as man to man. He had an extraordinary way of infecting strangers with his own enthusiasms, and they would go to great lengths to help him find anything on which he had set his heart.

But there was a man who played a trick on him, in these early days, and it was probably just as well that he did not find out till after he had left I-chang. One of his specimens which was accepted by the experts as a new discovery was named *Actinotinus sinensis* and illustrated in the *Icones Plantarum*, a Kew publication devoted to making known the best new plants. The picture aroused someone's suspicions. The specimen was more carefully scrutinized, and turned out to be a fake. Henry's assistant collector had, with Chinese dexterity, inserted the flower of a viburnum into the bud of a chestnut.

When Antwerp Pratt, the naturalist, was setting off on a long expedition through Sze-Chwan to the borders of Tibet, Henry persuaded him to take along one of the Chinese he had trained and collect plants on the way. He also secured for Kew the collection of the Rev. Ernst Faber, a German Protestant missionary, who travelled by boat up through the Gorges, perhaps to re-convert the converts of Father Delavay.

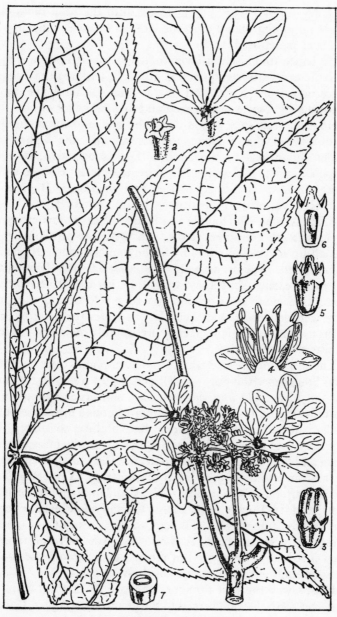

Actinotinus Sinensis

Henry himself was longing to get into the high mountains where no foreigner, not even the Roman Catholic missionaries, had ever penetrated.

He wrote to Thiselton-Dyer that Sir Robert Hart was sympathetic to scientific enquiries in all fields, and might agree to a suggestion from Kew, and grant him special leave to go collecting.[23] This was arranged and in 1888 he set off.

He made two long expeditions, the first into the mountains south-west of the Yangtze, the second into the higher and wilder mountains to the north. The second trip, into the Hupeh district, is described in bare outline in a letter which Thiselton-Dyer published in the *Kew Bulletin*.[24] It gives no hint whatever of the difficulties of the undertaking.

E. H. Wilson, who followed in Henry's footsteps twenty years later, says this country was the worst going in all China.[25] It was all up and down climbing of the toughest kind. It was not uninhabited. Roads actually existed, they had been made centuries earlier, but they were dug up and tilled by the peasants because level ground was so precious, and elsewhere they were left to the weather. It was easier to travel by footpaths used by smugglers. Henry presumably managed to forget he was a Customs man.

There was no wheeled traffic, and even ponies were not much use. Sometimes the only way of getting up was to hang on to the tail of a mule and be towed. A westerner had to bring with him the necessities of life, as there were no foreign goods to be had and the natives, indeed, had nothing to spare. The luggage could be carried by coolies, but the problem was to feed them and find them anywhere to sleep. The inns of the country were mean and dirty even by their standards. Yet it would not do to camp out. Wilson says, "The Chinese do not understand tents, and it is unwise to try innovations in a land where people are unduly inquisitive." The one thing you must not omit to bring was a sedan chair. A chair was a sign of respectability, even if it had to be carried in pieces. It was more use than a passport to the traveller in out-of-the-way parts.

Henry was the first foreigner the people of the mountains had ever seen. He conformed to the generally accepted Chinese idea of a demon, for though of average height he was tall by their standards, and was fair-haired and blue-eyed, and when in the wilds grew a fine red beard. Once when he had got ahead of his party on a mountain with an eerie reputation he met a party of natives who at sight of him dropped all they were carrying and fled. Yet they accepted him in the end so thoroughly that when Wilson came along all those years later he met with a welcome whenever he came to a place where Henry had been.

He gave himself no airs and put no strain on local hospitality. A cook and a couple of coolies were all his retinue. He cut all his wants to the minimum. All he says about it himself is, "I had a very pleasant trip, being on excellent terms with the people."[26]

The virgin forests began at three days' journey from I-chang. There were bears and wild boar and large monkeys, badgers, or something like them, an antelope as big as a cow, and several kinds of pheasants. Tigers were confined to the plains, but wolves and leopards were common. Henry says they attacked dogs but not men. "At I-chang the natives returning to their homes in the mountains were frequently followed by a solitary wolf, which was intent on seizing the dogs following the native party, and the caravan was followed at a distance by the leopards who were bent on getting possession of the dogs or the wolves."[27]

He had written to Thiselton-Dyer: "The Chinese also speak of a wild horse, described as being about the size of an ass, which formerly existed in this part of the range, and I have no doubt some animal of this kind (perhaps the origin of the 'unicorn') will be found."[28] If there had been a unicorn he should have been the person to catch it, for he had much in him of the "blessed fool" of Celtic folklore, the innocent, like the younger sons in fairy tales, who by courtesy and fair dealing gains the favour of the immortals.

To readers who will by now ask what he did find it is difficult to give a simple answer, for botany is a complex subject. Lists of his plants may be found in the *Index Florae Sinensis*, a catalogue which was begun in the eighteen-eighties by a committee of several learned bodies. When the seventh part came out in 1889 the *Kew Bulletin* commented: "There is some risk that it may be difficult to compress the undertaking within the modest limits which were at first contemplated."[29]

The high mountains of Hupeh turned out to be the native habitat of many of the vegetable drugs which were the first object of Henry's enquiries, for instance a kind of rhubarb which was cultivated round I-chang and was exported to England. He found there also many conifers, ten new maples, many roses and viburnums, and the wild original of the garden chrysanthemum. In the mountains, too, grow several varieties of lilies. Lilies are supposed to have originated farther north and to have been pushed south in the Ice Age, but this theory does not tally with their survival in the cold of these high altitudes.

Henry's discoveries threw light on many problems of plant distribution and opened up new lines of enquiry. He found many species which, though not new, were not known to grow in China. China turned out to be the original home of lilies, roses, rhododendrons, prunuses, pyruses, lonicera. In Hupeh he found a *Liriodendron*, or tulip tree, of which there are only two species, the other belonging to North America. Plant distribution in turn throws light on geology. Thus he helped to piece together a great mass of information bearing on the history of the earth.

The great majority of his finds are of little interest to gardeners. But some of them fitted in extremely well with the new ideas on gardening preached by William Robinson and Gertrude Jekyll. Nothing could be more suitable for naturalising in informal settings than wild plants from a temperate region like that round I-chang. *Lilium henryi* was one, a spectacular plant in cultivation, though in the wild Henry never found it growing more than waist high, or carrying more than four or five flowers. *Clematis henryi* and *Parthenocissus henryana* were common I-chang creepers. *Rhododendron augustinii* was brought in from the mountains by a native collector, and Henry found it in plenty on his first journey. From there too came several viburnums, the evergreen climber *Lonicera henryi*, and the useful little creeping perennial, *Corydalis thalictrifolia*, all of which are established in gardens now.

The high moment of Henry's first long expedition was the sight of *Davidia involucrata*. It was something he never forgot. Some fifty years later, after visiting a fine specimen at Mount Usher in Ireland, Mrs. Henry wrote: "I remember Augustine saying one of the strangest sights he saw in China, riding up a river valley, was *Davidia* in full blow on the other side, waving its innumerable ghost handkerchiefs."[30] The "handkerchiefs" are the large greenish white bracts which enclose the inconspicuous little flowers. In cultivation the leaves and bracts come together, a lovely combination of white and fresh spring green. But in the wild state, it seems, the flowers and bracts come before the leaves, and their appearance on bare branches must indeed be striking. The *Davidia* that Henry saw was an isolated one, sown by some strange freak far from its kind. The natives regarded it with veneration. In those rugged wastes it might well seem a supernatural vision. The mind's eye would create a nimbus round the branches hung with white in the sun.

Henry's name is not associated with *Davidia* as Father David had already sent home leaves and flowers from the Tibetan border. One of the difficulties of collecting is the time-lag between flower and seed time. Henry did secure fruit, but apparently not seed that would germinate. Ten years later he was still writing enthusiastically about the tree to Thiselton-Dyer, urging him to tell collectors to look out for it.[31] It was finally introduced to cultivation by E. H. Wilson.

He worked his way through the mountains at from eight to ten thousand feet till he came to the Yangtze again on the borders of Sze-Chwan. He came back by boat down the rapids, which must have made a splendid finish to the trip.

Kew had helped him to meet the expenses of these expeditions. Grants were made towards the cost of employing native collectors, £24 in June and a further £15 in July, which would go a long way as their wages were only about thirty shillings a month.[32] It is not clear whether at this stage Henry was paid for any of his specimens. There were no special funds for the purpose. Thiselton-Dyer put him in touch with other herbaria which bought duplicate sets from him, and as his reputation grew the demand for these increased. Kew always had the pick of his collections, and he presented the Gardens with a great deal. These first two journeys left him somewhat out of pocket.

This did not trouble him. He was not unbusinesslike, but he was very far from mercenary. Money was a tool, not an end in itself; scientific work brought its own reward. His philosophy is expressed in a quotation from Marcus Aurelius, in one of his later letters to Thiselton-Dyer: "What more dost thou want when thou hast done a service? Art thou not content that thou hast done something conformable to thy nature, and dost thou ask to be paid for it, just as if the eye demanded a recompense for seeing or the feet for walking?"[33]

Henry's first modest publication appeared in 1888 in the journal of the Chinese Royal Asiatic Society. It was a fifty-page supplement: *List of Chinese Plants with their colloquial names at I-chang.*

In this year Henry was elected a Fellow of the Linnean Society of London. This was a token of recognition of the value of his work. He had to be proposed and seconded by two people already Fellows, with an outline of his qualifications. Thiselton-Dyer saw to it, and paid his first subscription. It is pleasant to find that Henry reimbursed him with bulbs of *Lilium henryi.* The first of these, sent in March 1889, flowered at Kew the following August.[34]

Henry's explorations had opened up opportunities which he longed to exploit. He made plans for sending a Chinese collector out from I-chang to go more closely over some of this promising ground. Thiselton-Dyer sent another application to Sir Robert Hart for Henry's botanical services, but this time there was no reply.[35] However sympathetic the Inspector General of Customs was to science, the Service had many exigencies. This was a time when trade was developing and new stations were being opened. To Henry's disappointment he was transferred, in April 1889, to the unwholesome, fever-ridden, utterly unpleasant tropical island of Hainan.

Hainan is at the southernmost extreme of China. The civilised inhabitants were Chinese who had come back to settle there after making money in the Straits Settlements. They were more friendly to foreigners than the Chinese of the mainland. "One never heard the cry of Fan Qui—'foreign devil'—which was often yelled by runaway small boys in Canton."[36] They were in a way foreigners themselves. The natives of the island spoke a different language. A great deal of it was still unexplored. There were mountains and dense forests, inhabited by aborigines.

Tropical plants never attracted Henry as much as those of temperate zones. He proceeded, of course, to collect, and found some new species among about 750 specimens, but according to Mrs. Henry's notebook there was nothing very remarkable.

It was intensely hot and almost daily there were terrifying thunderstorms in which people were killed. A cholera epidemic broke out at the capital, four miles from the port, where Henry was. Every house had at least one death. The commander of the Chinese garrison marched in one day with half a dozen soldiers who were, he said, the sole survivors of six hundred men.

Henry was commissioned by Sir Robert Hart to go on a gunboat to the south of the island to investigate the illegal import of opium there. It would have been an adventure, and an opportunity to land on an unknown shore. Henry was looking forward to it, but he never went. The weather seemed to grow hotter, his appetite failed, he found himself living on lychees and tea. One day it occurred to him to take his own temperature: it was 104 degrees Fahrenheit. The same afternoon he was carried aboard a trading steamer which was going to Hong-Kong. It had a cargo of live pigs. Nine hundred pigs squealed rhythmically with the rolling of the boat, and the fever patient was soothed to sleep.

What he had was not cholera but pernicious malaria, which was endemic in Hainan. He recovered in a Hong-Kong hotel. It was during his convalescence that he heard from Kew the mortifying news about *Actinotinus sinensis* and there was nothing he could do about it then.[37]

In August, after eight years in China, he got his first home leave.

4

Henry went back to Europe via Japan and San Francisco, taking his time over it. He always enjoyed journeys. On

board ship he used to get up at 5 a.m. because he found that
early rising was a good way of making the acquaintance of the
captain. He never travelled without meeting odd or interesting
people.

He revelled in space and extremes—vast oceans, high
mountains, great cities. For seventeen days they steamed
across the Pacific. It was cloudy all the way, they passed no
other ship and saw neither sun nor stars. Then the captain
announced that in three hours' time they would see the coast
and would be somewhere near the Golden Gate. Sure enough,
in three hours they saw the lines of great waves breaking, and
were four miles north of the harbour. The impression of this
moment stayed with Henry, like the first sight of the *Davidia*.
Years later he dictated this note to Mrs. Henry: "It is impossible for any thinking person who has thus been conducted
across thousands of miles of the trackless ocean not to recognize
that there is absolute truth in science. Without mathematics
and astronomy it would be impossible."[38] These sciences may
be mere constructs of the human mind, but they get results.

Henry contrasted San Francisco unfavourably with Yoko-
hama: "The Japanese, quiet, graceful and highly civilized;
the Americans loud-talking or noisy, and seemingly very
vulgar."[39] The Japanese, who till the mid-eighteen-sixties
had been more isolated even than the Chinese, were in fact
westernising themselves at an astonishing rate and were
developing into a military power. But no one yet saw them as
a threat, and their art was the fashion in London and Paris.

The bustle and noise of America were extraordinary to
Henry. He fell in with a Canadian friend who had been ill and
saw him as far as his home in Toronto. On the way they
stopped at Chicago. They were invited to lunch in a hotel by
a business tycoon. After twenty minutes their host left them
in the care of the head waiter, explaining that he himself
could not afford to take more than a quarter of an hour
off for a meal. Toronto was a less hectic city and reminded
Henry of Edinburgh. He went from there to New York and
sailed in a small steamer with thirty passengers that crossed the
Atlantic in a fortnight.

He went home first. There is nothing to show how Ireland
struck him after his long absence. He probably found little

change. Agrarian agitation was on the increase and there were grim incidents from time to time, shootings that were not merely private acts of vengeance. But good Catholics like the Henrys had no truck with secret societies; these were for the ruined, the frustrated, the desperate. Neither did they share the worries of wealthy landlords.

Charles Stuart Parnell had taken the political stage. He had persuaded Gladstone of the necessity for Home Rule. One Home Rule Bill had been defeated, but it had been a near thing, and another was coming up. Before it was introduced, Parnell fell dramatically from power. He was cited as co-respondent in a divorce case, which finished his career. In retrospect it can be seen as a tragedy for Ireland. Without his leadership the Irish Parliamentary Party dithered and divided, the demands of patriots ran more and more to extremes, and more people's minds became familiar with the concept of freedom by violence.

But Henry had other things to think about. He thoroughly enjoyed his leave and at the end of it he married.

He did not spend much time at Tyanee. His grandmother, who presided there, had died two years before. He found his youngest sister ill in Belfast, and stayed to see her on the way to recovery. Then he went on to London and at last met Thiselton-Dyer.

He was surprised to find himself quite a celebrity. He was warmly welcomed at Kew. The Thiselton-Dyers invited him to stay. He found himself in an atmosphere wonderfully congenial to him, after the frustrations of China and the apathy in Ireland. Kew then felt itself at the heart of a great and growing organisation—the Kipling empire. Thiselton-Dyer was a live wire, newly come into the succession of the two great Hookers. In his time rubber plants from South America were first tried out in the East, and a Kew-trained man developed the cocoa industry of the Gold Coast. He and Henry had something in common. He, too, had begun as a medical student and after changing over to natural science had for two years been a Professor of Botany in Dublin. His wife, Sir Joseph Hooker's daughter, was a botanical illustrator. They were all three lifelong friends.

Antwerp Pratt's collections opportunely arrived. Henry and Thiselton-Dyer unpacked them together, and Henry

helped with the sorting of these and his own specimens. He
learnt a lot more about botany. He attended meetings of the
Linnean Society. He also took on a busman's holiday task at
the request of the London office of the Chinese Customs. They
were getting enquiries about plants producing textile fibres,
and handed them to the expert on the spot. There was the
usual confusion: products of different places being wrongly
given the same name; the same product going under different
names in different places. Henry did a *Memorandum on the Jute
and Hemp of China*.[40] He summed up what was known of the
subject and listed a number of points that needed clarifica-
tion. He distinguished seven separate plants that supplied
the Chinese with different qualities of grass cloth. Oddly
enough, they did not make linen out of flax, although they
used the seeds for oil.

But he did not spend all his time in learned scientific circles.
Evelyn Gleeson was in London, working at a studio called
Ludovici's, and with her he picked up the threads of the friendship of college days. Through her he met some of the "new
women" who were a much-talked-of phenomenon. Evelyn
herself was not aggressively advanced, but she was progressive.
She belonged to a women's club, the Pioneer Club.

A newspaper alleged that the Pioneer members dressed like
men. Evelyn defended them from the charge: "Men," she
wrote, "are fond of sneering and laughing at the advanced
woman, whom they condemn without knowing, but when
(as sometimes happens) they join the 'Pioneers' at a social
evening I am sure they must devoutly wish that advancement
were more general."[41]

Henry was never one of the mockers. His temperament was
conservative, and in politics he inclined somewhat to the right,
but he was always an upholder of women's rights. He enjoyed
mixing with the Pioneers.

In the summer he stayed with the Gleesons at Benown. It
was a typical large square Georgian house in wooded lands
going down to the shores of Lough Ree, in the very middle of
Ireland. There they were "innocently gay", a favourite
phrase of Henry's. He was sure life ought to be enjoyed. One
could not ignore the misery of it, but neither should one miss
the fun.

The pleasures of this holiday have been preserved like dried
flowers in a faded half sheet of doggerel:

"Verses written A.D. 1890 by various hands:
    The moon that burnishes the lake,
    The meteor dazzling in the night,
    The picnics, ruins and the cake,
    The store room and the elfin sprite.
    Benown, that looks upon the Shannon,
    Athlone, old bridge and rusty cannon,
    The bacon, sausages and sultan skipper,
    The absence of the excursion tripper. . . .

    The rows that frequently arise,
    The round towers in their awful size. . . .

    The claret jug that ne'er was broken
    The baccy Eve's detected smokin'. . . .

    The bounteous lady lovely roses budding
    The yacht afore fresh breezes scudding. . . .

    The Hexagon that kept out rain
    That has not then been built in vain.
    Miss Smith reclining at the helm,
    Luxurious chestnut, lime and elm.
    Kelly, who ornaments the bar,
    Decked gaily as a jolly tar.
    Ethel sitting on hampers of drink
    For which Henry now and then gives a wink. . . .

    The artful sketcher sought for 'contrasts' still
    And plied his facile brush o'er vale and hill. . . .

    The rides on the heaving and rolling car
    And the lovely damsels at the bazaar.
    The Doctor making such splendid punch
    And the ladies at the Sunday lunch. . . ."[42]

So it goes on, covering almost every diversion available to
Irish country dwellers.

Among the ladies there may have been a girl called Caroline Orridge who was also studying at Ludovici's. She was certainly there the following March, when Henry wrote to Thiselton-Dyer:

"Perhaps the place seems very fair to me as in the house where I am staying there is also on a visit the girl who is so brave as to be willing to accompany me to China."[43] There is a sad irony in this, he did not guess what bravery would be required.

There are some highly competent oil paintings by Caroline Orridge in the possession of Evelyn Gleeson's nieces, but they are not enough on which to estimate her talent. Henry thought she was a genius; he may have been partial. She was at least gifted and genuine. It was her individual vision that attracted him; her freshness of outlook and her candour. "She made life so interesting . . . her peculiar genius brightened and illuminated everything." "She spoke the thoughts that come into people's heads first, which people always smother and put the listener off with second thoughts, which are tactful, sweet. Alas! these second thoughts have not the value of those first quick flashes of intuition. . . . That is the fascination of the artist: he sees clearly. Most people have muddy media through which things are distorted and unclean."[44]

Caroline's family had a jewellery business in Bond Street, so presumably they were well-to-do. Henry was poor, but he was a celebrated explorer and a young man with a future. If her family had any doubts they seem to have been quickly overcome. Caroline liked the idea of going to China. She wanted to paint there.

Henry's father died a fortnight before the wedding, aged only sixty-six. But Henry's leave was up, the ceremony could not be postponed. They were married on June 20th, 1891, at St. George's, Bloomsbury, had a week somewhere in France, and then sailed from Marseilles for the east.

The tragedy developed on the lines of many Victorian novels and more rapidly. Caroline was consumptive. It was in keeping with her artistic gifts. Apparently no one suspected it. She had influenza before the wedding, and then a cough, which got no better on the voyage out. At Singapore she had a haemorrhage. Henry got her into a hospital at Saigon, and after four weeks she was allowed to travel on. She was a semi-invalid when they reached Shanghai.[45]

5

The story of the next three years is the alternation of hopes and fears for Caroline, of Henry's efforts to save her, and of matters going from bad to worse in the Chinese empire.

Just before Henry went on leave there came a turn of events in China which the western diplomatists all thought very much for the best: the Emperor came of age and the Dowager Empress retired. Go-ahead nineteenth-century businessmen rejoiced to think that the further opening up of the country would now be easier. They saw it as inevitable, and all to the good for the Chinese as well as themselves.

Between the Chinese and the Westerners there was an abysmal lack of understanding. To the Westerners, Chinese customs were "the ways that are dark and the tricks that are vain".[46] The Chinese thought the foreigners simply brash.

The workings of Chinese bureaucracy, with all the petty rules and regulations it had accumulated, and its opportunities for bribery and rake-offs, struck most Westerners as inefficient and absurd. So it is interesting to find that Sir Robert Hart took a different view. He alone gave the Chinese credit for knowing their own business.

"China needs neither imports nor exports and can do without foreign intercourse. . . . The eighteen provinces of China proper—each of them as large as and many of them more populous than most European states—afford room enough for every kind of operation and transaction. Government taxation has always and everywhere been of the lightest possible kind, and what are called 'squeeze' have been either legitimate collections other than the dues and duties foreign trade tariffs published, or such variable amounts as traders have compounded for between their own offer and the sum the collector would consent to accept *below* the rate fixed by the tariff concerned. Very wealthy individuals have, from time to time, been called on for special and occasionally large contributions during periods of national difficulty. But on the whole trade has not been charged beyond what it could afford to pay. When a tax looks like becoming too heavy, traders simply close their establishments as a protest, and the local officials soon remedy the matter; and it is curious to see how, in this weakest and yet toughest of empires, age and experience have worked out what may be styled automatic action to keep the huge machine in order."[47]

The grit in the works of the machine, some of it, consisted of foreign currency. Though China had invented paper money centuries earlier it had, in the late nineteenth century, no regular coinage. Payments were made in weighed-out amounts of gold and silver, sometimes in bolts of silk. Paper money was issued in terms of silver bullion. Dollars of several countries were circulating, but these too had to be weighed. The most popular unit of value was the tael of silver, about one and one-third ounces avoirdupois. That summer the ups and downs of silver made business chaotic. Henry told Thiselton-Dyer: "Make contracts for 3s. to the dollar and in a month when the goods arrive the rate may be 2s. 9d."[48] What with this, and the hope of getting new concessions out of the young Emperor, Shanghai was one huge gambling den.

Meanwhile the Dowager Empress had quietly appropriated the funds allocated to the Chinese Navy for the purpose of restoring the Summer Palace, which had been burnt down by the allied powers in the disturbed time of 1861. The Emperor had given it to her for a residence, hoping perhaps to keep her quiet, but it did not take up all her time. While western diplomats tried to gain the ear of the Emperor's official ministers, the Empress kept in very much closer touch with everything that went on through the palace eunuchs. Some of them were men of high intelligence. They had risen from being mere under-cover agents and even held positions of state. They were of the reactionary party in the government. The Westerners underrated them.

Away from Peking anti-foreign feeling showed more openly. There had been serious riots along the Yangtze. Henry

expected to be sent to another port. With Caroline ill, the
country disturbed, and their destination unsettled, he had
enough to worry about. After a few weeks, however, he was
appointed Assistant Officer in the Imperial Customs headquarters at Shanghai.

Henry saw no further into the Chinese situation than the
ordinary man in the street. In a letter to Thiselton-Dyer he
put the view of most Shanghai officials and business men.
"My idea is that the riots on the Yangtze are caused by the anti-
foreign party in the state with a view to making foreigners
uncomfortable and stopping the further opening up of the
country, which does away with the mandarins' emoluments
from taxes on native trade. This party has cleverly worked
under the screen of an imaginary rebellious society and the
Chinese government has let things go on. No act of injustice
has been perpetrated by any European to cause these riots
and proper reparations ought to be exacted."[49]

The Henrys took a flat on the Bund, with a view of the shipping, and furnished it with bamboo and Chinese crockery,
sensibly making the most of what they could buy cheaply on
the spot, and opting for elegant bareness, like the interiors of
Japan. Henry's taste was austere for those days of draperies
and bric-a-brac. He said a living-room ought not to look like
a shop.

Caroline could not take much part in social life. Invalids
were almost unknown in the active bustle of the treaty ports.
Death, when it came, was usually sudden. The awful presence
of typhoid and cholera actually gave a zest to life, like the
skeletons at Egyptian feasts. Shanghai kept up its amusements:
cricket, shooting, boating, tandem-driving, racing. Sir Robert
Hart had a horse called Fenian, and was accused by a crank of
not being a loyal British subject.

In the spring Caroline was better, and went on a trip with
Henry in a Revenue cruiser to the islets in the mouth of the
Yangtze. But the hot summer did her no good, and in July he
sent her to Japan for a change of air.

Henry as usual took refuge in work. There were no opportunities for plant hunting round Shanghai, but he compiled
some *Notes on Chinese Economic Botany* which were published in a
limited edition of a hundred copies by a missionary paper called

The Shanghai Messenger. Some years later this inconspicuous work attracted the attention of the United States Department of Agriculture. It was photo-lithographed and circulated to U.S. officials in China, with no profit to the author since there was no copyright protection.[50]

The opening of new trading stations in southern China was providing a rich new field for botanists. Henry wrote to Thiselton-Dyer that "Hancock at Meng-tsz has a splendid opportunity to collect. I tried to stir him up."[51] He was one day to follow in Hancock's footsteps. Hosie,[52] the British consul at Tamsui, in Formosa, was following up the investigation of textile fibres. Even poor Caroline did a little collecting in Japan.

She came back in October somewhat better. Hoping to find a climate that would suit her, Henry applied for transfer to the island of Formosa, and was posted as Assistant Officer at Takao.

Formosa was then almost an unknown island. The Dutch had settled there in the past, and in the seventeenth century had been driven out by the Chinese who had been driven out of China by the Manchus. These forerunners of President Chiang Kai-shek submitted in 1683, and since then the island had been part of the empire, an appendage which looked as if it might again become detached. Several of the powers had toyed with the idea of relieving the Chinese of this outlying possession. American experts had prepared a long report on it, which had been shelved owing to the Civil War. The French had fought there during a private war with China in the eighteen-eighties, but had evacuated the island again. It was a beautiful place, but had a dangerous coast. There were lurid tales of the fate of shipwrecked crews at the hands of savages in the wilder parts.

The Chinese had control of the north and the fertile western plain, but the mountains to the east and south were inhabited by different savage tribes who lived by hunting and by war with the Chinese and each other. Travel into the interior was impossible. There were no roads; communication between the principal towns was by sea. A handful of Europeans, mainly consular and Customs men, lived in each of the half-dozen trade centres.

Takao, where the Henrys were, is within the tropics, but its climate was pleasant, never too hot or too cold. The harbour was a big lagoon. Henry built a house on a cliff overlooking the harbour entrance. Porpoises were to be seen in the lagoon. On the banks of a river flowing into it there were trees with oysters clinging to their branches. Not far away were mangrove swamps. Inland there was a mountain, Apes Hill, where a Mr. Playfair, a British consul, had collected about four hundred species of plants.

Henry had given up medicine when he took up his appointment at the Shanghai headquarters, but on arrival at Takao his first job was to help at the post mortem on his predecessor, who had died of fever. His chief was a martyr to sciatica, and he found he would have to do most of the work of the Customs. But he had to begin collecting again. His enthusiasm had been redoubled by his visit to London. He took to going out at 4 a.m. He would climb Apes Hill by sunrise and put in two hours collecting before breakfast. Dawn on the beautiful island was rewarding, but there were cobras in the clefts of the rocks. He took along a couple of spaniels which smelt the snakes out and drove them off.

The plains were too richly cultivated to contain rare plants. The mangrove swamps were disappointing. Henry cast longing eyes on the mountains, where from Takao one could see the savages' camp fires. He got as far as a village called Bankimsing in the foothills, and engaged some natives to bring him every kind of fruit and flower, but they were afraid to go into the mountains. He remarks bitterly in a letter to Thiselton-Dyer that they were too careful of their heads.[53]

There were more friendly tribes in the south of the island, and a chance came to visit them when Henry had to make an official call at the lighthouse on the South Cape. The Customs was responsible for all the lighting of the coast. Caroline went with him, and so did another European couple. It was a holiday trip, a happy interlude in those years of alternation between hope and despair. The lighthouse was occupied by two or three Europeans and half a dozen Chinese. The natives lived by agriculture instead of hunting, and they were all on good terms.

This was Henry's first encounter with really primitive people. The Chinese whom he had met in the high mountains of Hupeh were not primitive; they were the remains of former civilization. He was struck by the contrast:

"We visited the Koaluts, a tribe who twenty years ago murdered a ship's crew and have only lately given up head-hunting. They live in delightful houses, so clean and pretty."[54]

"There is no necessary connection between progress in handicrafts and progress in the greater arts of civilization. Many savages make beautiful things. The word savage is an unfortunate one; it connotes too much. In the south of Formosa there is a hunting tribe which I visited; they killed twenty years ago the captain and his wife and crew of an American barque and have been noted for savage acts of cruelty. Their houses were the perfection of neatness and cleanliness, built of wood with long eaves and a court-yard in front clean as a parlour table; and little piles of firewood so symmetrically arranged. Now the Chinese have attained much civilization and they have dirty, dusty houses, horrible clothes very often, and in a word are vulgarly dirty."[55]

Faithful to his hobby, Henry interested the lighthouse keepers in plants, and under their guidance one of these same savages made an excellent collection.

Later on he went again, by himself, to the south cape on business and got further inland. He brought presents to the savages, ostensibly from the Emperor, to reward them for rescuing a shipwrecked crew, and to confirm them in their reformed ways. He invited them to come and receive the presents and entertained them at a feast, followed by dances which went on for hours. These natives were very handsomely dressed. Those in the forests were much more savage. Henry was invited to a feast by another agricultural tribe. Mrs. Henry's notebook says: "After a good deal of difficulty and the making of what practically amounted to a treaty, A. went on and visited a purely hunting tribe who had no agriculture whatever. These people were approached by a march of several hours through the jungle, the tortuous path would have been quite impossible to find without the guide who was sent to conduct the party. They were allowed to see the village of this tribe but all the young men and young women had disappeared into the forest and they were received by an old man and an old woman who offered them nothing to eat but simply showed the houses."⁵⁶ These houses too were neat and attractive.

Once, on Formosa, the notebook says, "A. saw a large canoe full of Polynesian people, about a dozen men and two or three women. They were blown away from their native island about 4,000 miles away. No one knew how long they had been on board. No one could understand their language, so they were taken in charge by the consul. As soon as a man-of-war came they were put on board and taken to Hong-Kong. But nobody there could find out whence they came. So the man-of-war cruised all over the Pacific until ultimately it found the island which the natives recognised and repatriated them. The distance was so great that they must have been weeks at sea. The barque was a long narrow one and had carried a great many more than the thirteen or fourteen survivors. Being practically amphibious they had dived for fish which served as food, they drank the rain water caught during the journey."⁵⁷

Such was the solicitude of civilized man for the savage when their interests did not clash. Now there are hardly any aborigines left in Formosa, and their chief resource is to dress up and dance for tourists.

The British Foreign Office was following the example of the Americans and preparing a report on Formosa. Henry contributed an appendix on the flora and economic botany, which was reprinted in the *Kew Bulletin*. This became amplified into his *List of Plants from Formosa*, published by the Asiatic Society of Japan, the first work on the general botany of the whole island. He had help with the flowers of the north of the island from Hosea B. Morse, his opposite number in the Customs there, and the lighthouse keeper and the savage covered the south, but the native at Bankimsing still refused to risk having his own head collected, and the list was not as full as Henry would have liked. Nevertheless, his book, published in 1896, remained the sole authority for the next ten years, and the next study to appear was based on it.

Henry listed 1,482 plants, with the localities in which they occurred and their economic uses, if any. The product for which he saw most future was camphor. He wrote a couple of papers on it for the *Pharmaceutical Journal* of London, and sent Thiselton-Dyer a bottle of camphor oil. He also sent the *Kew*

Bulletin a note on Shu-lang root or dye-yam, which the fisher-
men used for dyeing their nets. Camphor became one of
Formosa's chief exports.

Henry's 1893 letters to Thiselton-Dyer all contain pathetic
bulletins on Caroline's health. In May she seemed no better. In
June the weather was dry and she was feeling well. In July
it was clear that she must have a better climate, and by October
it had been arranged for her to go to Denver in Colorado.
Henry's sister Mary, the one who seems to have been the
closest to him in affection, volunteered to go with her. Mary
Henry had trained as a nurse. They left at the end of January.
    Henry's reputation as a botanist had spread. He now tried,
for the only time in his life, to cash in on it. He had been given
an introduction to Professor Sargent, head of the Arnold
Arboretum of Harvard and editor of the leading American
gardening periodical *Garden and Forest*. In May 1894 he wrote
to him:
    "The chief object of my addressing you, is in reference to my
herbarium which I wish to dispose of; and please allow me
briefly to enter into some personal explanations. My wife
suffers from phthisis and has been now in Colorado (with great
benefit) for three or four months. I have almost determined
on throwing up my position here . . . and trying my fortunes
in Colorado. This will necessarily prevent me from continuing
my botanical work, as I shall have a very uphill fight, I
imagine, in America. So I think of disposing of my herbarium;
and I should prefer that it would go to an American institution.
The Kew people have duplicates of it all. Harvard has already
purchased a set of my Central China plants."
    Details of the collection follow. Henry adds: "It is with
the greatest reluctance that I am thinking of parting with this
collection; but I can't afford to keep it. Many of the specimens
are type-specimens; they are the duplicates on which numerous
new species and some twenty new genera have been founded.
The herbarium at Kew has a complete set of all these specimens
of mine; and in view of the close connection between the flora
of the Eastern States and China, I think it will be most ad-
vantageous if these specimens of mine should go to America,
rather than to Europe."[58]

Sargent wrote back encouragingly. American botanists were ready to jump at such an offer.

That summer, war broke out between Japan and China. Henry wrote to Thiselton-Dyer, "The Japanese are keen to have a fight anywhere. In many ways they are the French of the East."[59] Their politeness and elegance were outweighed now by their military efficiency. The Chinese navy was impoverished by the Dowager Empress's extravagance. Too late she cancelled her sixtieth birthday celebrations at the Summer Palace and embarked on a programme of austerity. The Japanese fleet gained easy victories off Korea. In Formosa warnings were received from Peking that the island might any day be invaded. The air was full of contradictory rumours. Wealthy residents began to leave. Henry was afraid he might be trapped. He had applied for a year's leave, hoping to resign at the end of it if he could find an opening in Colorado. He packed his books and collections, hoping to be off before the Japanese came. In September, just as he was about to leave, a telegram came from his sister to say that Caroline had died.[60]

Poor Caroline Henry! She had moved all too swiftly through the fair. It was years before Henry could become reconciled to her loss. He made things worse for himself by morbid imaginings. Two years later he wrote to Evelyn Gleeson: "I think I might have saved her had I fought more strenuously, if I had taken the decision to leave China sooner."[61] He had been ready to throw up all his prospects, and it would have been useless, yet his mind kept going back over the circumstances. He was stunned by the blow.

> "So fled her beauty leaving dim
> The emptying chambers of his heart. . . ."

The lines are by A. E. (George Russell), a friend of Henry's later days. They come from a poem called *Endurance*. After describing most movingly the sense of loss experienced by one in Henry's state, the poem changes its mood. The descant runs:

> "He walked at night along the sands,
> He saw the stars dance overhead,

He had no memory of the dead
But lifted up exultant hands
To hail the future like a boy,
The myriad paths his feet might press.
Unhaunted by old tenderness
He felt an inner secret joy—
A spirit of unfettered will
Through light and darkness moving still
Within the All to find its own,
To be immortal and alone."

Padraic Colum, a younger poet and friend, remembers reading this in Henry's presence. It stuck in his mind because he noticed that Henry was deeply affected.[62] That was in another hemisphere and Henry had remarried, very happily, and none of his circle of new friends had ever heard of Caroline. Life goes on and time does heal, however slow the process.

As there was now no point in his resigning, Henry wrote to Professor Sargent again in October to explain that he was only sending half the material he had originally offered, as he wanted to keep enough type specimens to form a nucleus of future collections. He said, if Sargent wished, he would collect specially for him without payment, if Sargent would recoup the expense of employing natives. "The only point is this, that I wish Kew to have the describing of new species. They are engaged in the compilation of the *Index Florae Sinensis*, and have the best Chinese collection to make comparison with."[63] So he laid down the principles governing his relations with these two leading herbaria of the Old and New World. Sargent, like Thiselton-Dyer, became a lifelong friend.

The Japanese did not invade Formosa; the Chinese ceded it to them by treaty. There was a little trouble when they arrived to take over. The Formosan Chinese made a foolish vain attempt to set up an independent republic. Henry's friend Hosea Morse showed good sense and bravery by refusing to hoist the republican flag. The island remained under Japanese rule till the end of the Second World War. Its development progressed rapidly and ruthlessly.

6

Henry went on leave before the change-over in Formosa. He may have gone home to Tyanee but cannot have spent long there, for he devoted most of this year to studying law. He attended lectures, ate dinners for the requisite number of terms, passed an examination in Roman Law and became a member of the Middle Temple.[64]

He may have "plunged in" (a favourite phrase) to this before Caroline died, with the idea of turning lawyer in America. After her death it filled an urgent need for mental distraction. It led nowhere. He never practised, although he was still a member of the Middle Temple in 1928. The only advantage he ever seems to have derived from this entrance into the legal profession was that years later he succeeded in surprising the eminent Judge, Sir Walter Phillimore, when he happened to be staying with him. He confided in Miss Gleeson:

"I delivered myself of an opinion on American law which was correct and upset rather some authority that was being quoted on the subject. It is rather amusing to know out-of-the-way things."[65]

It was a deviation from his true path, but it helped him over the first months of loneliness.

In London he had to face his wife's relations. There was no unkindness. A Mr. Hull, husband of Caroline's sister, was helpful in matters of business, and continued to do small commissions for Henry for many years.

He strengthened ties with other friends, such as the Thiselton-Dyers, but his chief source of moral support was Evelyn Gleeson, who played the part of an understanding, undemanding confidante. Through her he came in contact with Irish doings in London, such as the Irish Literary Society, founded by W. B. Yeats in 1891.

On his way home he had made a new acquaintance whom he wished very much to introduce to his friend Evelyn, since he thought they could help each other. It was perhaps a pity he never succeeded. They were both Irish, but with a difference. The genus in those days had very distinct species which it was a delicate task to cross.

Henry's new friend was Miss Charlotte Payne-Townshend, the Protestant Anglo-Irish heiress who afterwards married George Bernard Shaw. Born in the same year as Henry, she had grown up in the south as he in the north, and at about the time he left Ireland for China her family had moved to England. Charlotte had been brought out in English Society, and all her life had done the rounds of London seasons and country house visits. Bored with all this, she varied it by travel. She was rich, and her own mistress, and at a loose end.

Charlotte felt herself to be Irish. She came of the caste to which Ireland then belonged, but she did not belong to the country in the sense that Henry did. She was aware of this, and what interested her in him may have been the novelty of finding a person she could talk to, who saw from another angle the problems of their native land. As it turned out, they had still more in common. They were both, just then, in a very similar state of mind.

For both of them the world had recently been drained of interest by the removal of one person. Henry, though lonely and remorseful, was respectably bereaved. Charlotte was in a more ambiguous position. She was struggling to overcome an infatuation with Axel Munthe, the celebrated Swedish doctor and well-known member of what would now be called the international set. He was a magnetic personality, and more than one woman found him *un homme fatal*. Charlotte was an attractive woman. She had had several suitors, but Axel Munthe was the only man to whom she herself had ever felt attracted, and she had just wakened up to the fact that he was not in the least in love with her.

She and Henry, therefore, were two middle-aged people who had each had a glimpse of the joy of loving and seen it vanish. She did not tell him her story; she did not need to. He divined that something had gone wrong. A vein of self-pity in him increased his sensitivity to other sorrows. They were both reflective and introspective. They discussed the meaning of life and the sickness of their souls, and the chance of doing something to bring happiness to others, if one had renounced it for oneself. Charlotte's biographer, Janet Dunbar, discovered among her papers two letters signed "Augustine Henry", and from the general style and tone, with no other clue to the identity of the writer, concluded that they were from a woman friend.

He certainly thought Miss Townshend stood much in need of advice, for she had a large private fortune and was toying with the idea of using it to promote the aims of the Socialist Party, which was then coming into prominence. Two years earlier Henry had written to Thiselton-Dyer: "Of course socialism is a fraud, it is the refuge of sickish people who are weak and don't get on in the race."[66] He had an antipathy to it derived from a combination of upbringing and experience. It led, he thought, to a state of bureaucratic paralysis such as existed in China. It ran counter to his notions of evolution and the survival of the fittest. He had also a feeling, arising out of his early religious training, that socialists laid too much stress on the things of this world and reckoned progress solely in terms of material gain.

So he warned Miss Townshend against impulsive generosity: "You must be very wise to do good."[67] The important thing was to fulfil oneself: "Make for yourself the brightest life, the best life possible; you will do more good that way than by throwing away cheerfulness."[68]

He thought she needed sensible women friends, like Evelyn Gleeson. It may just have crossed his mind that Miss Townshend could afford to become a patroness of the arts. But between Miss Townshend's territory and Miss Gleeson's there were invisible fences which only an unconventional soul like Henry could ignore. By the time he left London, in the autumn of 1895, the ladies still had not met.

He wrote to Evelyn Gleeson from Southampton: "I had a farewell note from Miss Townshend. She says she will look you up when she returns to town. (This is for you alone—she is, *I guess*, in sore *trouble*.) I have asked you many favours, too many. Now lavish your sympathy and kindness on her. That is my last asking. She is Irish, you know."[69]

Almost a year later, after several times recurring to the subject in letters, he wrote: "As for Miss Townshend, perhaps you will never see her, which would be most stupid on both your

E

parts, as you could help her and be interested in her. I saw very little of her indeed, but she made more impression on me than almost anyone in a curious sort of way, i.e., I was impelled to stand by her if necessary. She is very clever and intelligent and limpidly truthful, but her knowledge of the world seemed small."[70] And two months later: "As for the 'Fairy Princess', Miss Townshend, I hope you will meet her some day. I do not expect to do so myself, as I could not understand why she should take any interest in me. I think her ideals are not made for this world and told her so. But I shall always remember her as a most wonderful human soul."[71]

By that time Henry was as far away from London as anyone could go. He did meet Miss Townshend again, but he never succeeded in bringing her into Miss Gleeson's orbit. Years later, when there was another lady whom Henry thought eligible for Evelyn Gleeson's friendship, he reminded her of Miss Townshend, "who married Bernard Shaw and escaped into a non-Irish sphere".[72]

So he was bound again for China, and though the prospect was drearier than ever, the journey back revived his spirits. He did love to be on the move. On board ship he was always relaxed, observant and gay. A letter he wrote while crossing the Atlantic demands to be quoted in full:

U.S.M.S. *St. Louis*
15 November, 1895.

"Dear Evelyn,
    It is somewhat hard to write on shipboard; we have fine weather to-day, but the great ship is being pushed through the water at such a rate that all its parts vibrate and shake, as if it were going to pieces. It has been stormy and rough till now. We are about 150 in the first class, chiefly Americans going back from the wonderland of Europe. Much does one hear of the pyramids, Rome, Pisa, Venice and lovely Paris—of London and England little is said. The Americans are strangely non-English in spite of their descent. The Celt has revived in Hy Brazil, and there is not an American woman on board who is not suggestive of either Co. Cork or Rouen. We have about a dozen tall graceful Englishmen

of tender years and Lady P . . . [illegible] and her family of girls represent the Saxon dames on board with quiet manners, demure faces and exceptional dress.

"My table is not very remarkable. Opposite me sits a young Philadelphian demonstrator who has been studying brain and nerve in Paris and Vienna. His face is pale and haggard and he is devoted to science. His wife and her sister accompany him, quiet people of Puritan stock, mince features and jet black hair.

"Everyone was seasick the first two days, myself included, for the first time in my travels I had my slender meals on deck. On the third day nearly everyone came round. I cured two ladies by a little common-sense treatment. One a New York young matron I found in the morning at the head of the stairway decidedly pale. She had fainted twice in her cabin and had crawled up more dead than alive. I carried her on deck, put her in a chair, ordered her an under-done chop and forced her to eat it. In an hour she was the merriest rosy-cheeked one on board. Another was a Chicago girl with fascinating American manners, pretty feet and charming accent. She revived under the same treatment. I had a good deal of talk with her that day, but since then I have not had a word, she is engaged in conquering the six tall young Englishmen and has completely forgotten my existence.

"My chief talks have been with active men. One a Lieutenant in the U.S. army, a man of 40, half-grey, immensely broad, strongly common sense and full of just opinions. He has been in Europe looking up military matters there. He has been fairly talkative and much has he discoursed on frontier 'scapes, Chicago riots, Indians and the like. Another is a Paymaster in the U.S. Navy, just come from Buenos Ayres with a pretty wife and child. He is not quite as nice as the soldier. Another is a Scotchman, a mining and financial man, who talks with great gravity on great affairs of state and narrates curious experiences of Planchette, ghosts and dreams. Another, a young Californian cigar manufacturer, irrepressible, kind, frank to folly. He never tires of speaking of his home, of his funny old mother and his half dozen sisters, whom he worships. There is the usual number of Dutch or German-American bagmen, vulgar, poker-playing and deadly dull, with no more soul than a calf. There is an artist, Bryant, an American young man who has won several prizes in Paris and had three pictures in this year's Salon. He is small, nervous, young and very practical.

"The black 'Patti' is in the second cabin, where there have been two concerts. We are going to have our concert to-night. We have a music-hall troupe, three girls and three boys, who are much in evidence about eleven at night, smoking cigarettes, eating caviare and ices mixed, and generally rowdy in a non-disagreeable way. They will appear tonight with violins, mandolins, guitars, etc.

"There is a capital library on board. I have done a lot of reading—Landor, Froude's Caesar, Montaigne, two or three scientific books. There is even a work on botany but I haven't bothered with that.

"I have never been so lonely at times, and I cannot tell how horrible my sense of loss has been. They are all so poor who are alive compared with the one who is dead. She was so wonderful a spirit. I shall be so glad to get to work again. I did feel happy those weeks I was studying law.

November 16
"The pilot has come on board, his boat was No. 6. He wore a soft hat and put his left foot first on deck. On these details some money changed hands. The day is lovely. The little birds are out at sea from the land.

"Last night the concert came off, a programme of which is enclosed. Orlando Harley is a distinguished tenor, and sang very well. Miss Bessie Bellwood is a low music-hall person who sang two vulgar songs in a half-inebriated state. It's a weird thing, a concert at sea. Today everyone is very blithe and gay with the knowledge that land is so near. Warm affections bind most of the people to some in the States. The Lieutenant, Paymaster and I have drunk eternal friendship in Manhattan cocktails. Mrs. Montgomery is as merry as a bird, and we had great chaff at luncheon. I joined her table, saying I was tired of my own where my sayings were not appreciated. The Chicago girl and I have

cut each other dead. Either she cut me or I her; and the
fault will not be known where it is till the day of judgment.
What a haughty, beautifully chiselled, nervous, intelligent
face she has, a beautifully poised head and neck. It is not
exactly beauty, but it is brightness of soul as shown by the
eyes, balance of brain as shown by the nicely-shaped head.
"I will write no more now but say good-bye!
                    Yours ever truly,
                         Austin Henry.
    "P.S. The scene on the docks at Customs examination on
Sat. night indescribable. Spent till midnight roaming about
in search of distressed damsels' baggage. Chicago girl met
by her brother, a muff—couldn't get her baggage any-
how. I bribed a porter and found it in a minute. The day of
judgment arrived. She thanked me with the most winning
smile. We said good-bye.
    "Go on to Chicago to-morrow but don't stay there an
hour. Will soon be in Denver and see Mary who has just
replied to my telegram. It is now midnight. Have just
had kidneys and the longest lager with my cousin, the
editor.[73] Have been talking all day to him and others. Have
really got off so many paradoxical statements! New York is
wonderfully unlike an English city. It is a great Dublin,
Marseilles and half Paris rolled into one. I long to tell you of
Mr. O'Rourke, the Customs examiner, whose son is going
to be a priest, and how I passed, in consultation over the
wrongs of Ireland, my baggage. He never opened a
package."[74]

This is Henry in top form as a correspondent. He could be
sentimental, repetitive, prolix. When he had no one to talk to
letter writing was his chief indulgence. His pen rambled on,
relieving his mind of all its burdens. His letters are always
revealing, and often delightful. It is no wonder people kept
them. He sometimes thought of becoming a professional
writer. He had the material; he felt the urge. Alas! Whenever he addressed himself to an unknown public his spon-
taneity evaporated. His scientific conscience took over, his
writing became factual, colourless and dry. This is all the more
a pity because much of what other people wrote about China

struck him as false. He respected the accounts of experienced consular officials such as Hosie, Baber and Bourne, but detested popular writers. One much-quoted journalist whose works are in the bibliography of the chapters on China in the *Cambridge Modern History* was Henry's *bête noire*: "Colquhoun's two books *Across Chrysê* and *Among the Shans* are feeble productions. I hate superficial work of this kind; it is hardly worth coming so far to do so little."[75]

7

In Shanghai Henry fell into a prolonged depression. He attributed it to an attack of influenza, but the influenza may equally well have been brought on by strain. He had last lived there with Caroline and everything recalled her presence. He arrived also to find a family of old friends plunged in tragedy. The Cork doctor who had befriended him on his first arrival fifteen years before had died during the summer, and Henry was in time to attend the funeral of his widow. A colleague with whom he had arranged to share a house went to hospital with typhoid. There was always so much illness in these half-European half-Chinese cities. The sanitation was appalling, and according to Henry it was made worse by putting down European drains.[76] Hong-Kong had recently been devastated by plague.

Yet Shanghai for the Europeans generally was neurotically gay. Business was now booming, as the result of a new treaty which allowed foreigners to build factories. They built them, of course, on borrowed money, by means of joint stock companies, and this to the Chinese was another disreputable innovation. Borrowing, in old China, was an affair of primitive usury, something to be ashamed of, only resorted to if you were deep in debt.

China as a whole was in much the same position as an old-fashioned company with undervalued assets threatened by a huge take-over bid. Chinese families piled up unproductive gold reserves, while capital flowed in from other countries.

Henry, who became a shade more imperialist when writing to Thiselton-Dyer than he did with Evelyn Gleeson, told the former, "I see no signs of the decadence of Britain here. The other nations are still far behind in commerce and enterprise."[77]

Politically, Russia was in the lead. In Korea, where the war between China and Japan had started (it had been a puppet state of both) there had been a *coup d'état*, the Queen had been murdered, the King had taken refuge in the Russian legation, Japan was out and Russia was in. German diplomatists, hoping to distract Russia from competition in Europe, encouraged the Czar to think he had a mission to spread Christendom in the Far East.

Diplomacy was carried on in Peking. Shanghai was a commercial city, "practically a little republic", Henry wrote. "The government might be interesting but the people are all-too-much wayfarers. There are no questions of socialism or the like to amuse people's minds. Each one here believes firmly in the right of might, in the struggle for existence, and they are keen and lawless in business. Morals are in abeyance."[78]

"I really think China is soporific on the intellect. The great mass of human beings, the Chinese, practically unimpressionable, weigh on one like a dull leaden sky. Everyone takes refuge from the climate, physical and mental, in dissipation: the women go in for endless calls, gossip, scandal, balls; the men smoke and drink, ride and play games, have races, eat a lot, go in for voluntary fire-brigades. In fact they are very fine muscular athletic fellows with their senses highly developed, and don't strain their brains save on questions of shares and exchange."[79]

The day he arrived he was given tickets for a French play by a colleague who appeared with his moustache cut off, having been to a fancy dress ball. Then there was an amateur production of *The Gondoliers* followed up by a burlesque of it in which men took the women's parts. There were no "new women" in Shanghai, but there were all the older varieties. "The grass widows here are rather distressing," wrote Henry to Evelyn. "Indeed, upon my word, Rudyard Kipling is not a whit too severe in his treatment of Indian society."[80]

It had crossed his mind to ask his sister Mary to live with him, but it would have been a poor life for her. There was another objection. Mary Henry was a devout Catholic, Austin a lapsed one. He did not want to distress her by his scepticism. The climate of Shanghai was not that of faith.

The Customs officials did not share in the prosperity of the boom town. Inflation had reduced the value of their salaries and there were many resignations from the Service. Henry saw no chance of his work ever becoming interesting, and that it was unprofitable in addition did not make it pleasanter. He had no heart even for botany. No one else took any interest in it, and he had not the energy to begin.

He could only look on his present existence as an expiation. As he told his wife's friend, "I recognise very clearly how absurd for me was that dream of happiness with Caroline; and I failed then in that bravery and steadfastness of purpose which might have saved her life. My idleness and want of constant persistent energy has rendered my life barren of result. My knowledge of all things is of the half kind, useless."[81]

This was morbid. Deliverance, when it came, took a form which most people would have regarded as a judgment. He was appointed to Meng-tsz in South Yunnan, one of the remotest posts in the Customs. Henry welcomed the change. In May, 1896, he wrote to Evelyn Gleeson: "To Shanghai's vulgarity, vanity and vice I am bidding farewell."[82]

Meng-tsz was a Customs post that had been opened six or seven years before on the newly-defined frontier between French Indo-China and the Chinese province of Yunnan. The history of this region was typical of the foreign habit of nibbling round China's borders. Tonking, with the neighbouring kingdom of Annam, had been dependencies of the Chinese empire, and China's failure to keep order there had given the French an excuse to move in. After some years of fighting and muddled negotiation, France had taken over all the country south of the Red river, promising to defend the southern frontier of China if the Chinese would put down rebels operating across the border. The country was now settling down and the local banditry were officially dispersed.

The Red river came down from the mountains of Sze-Chwan, almost providing a link with the upper reaches of the Yangtze. The French had taken control of its navigation, and

done away with petty Chinese restrictions. As a result the
river had become a main trade route into southern China,
even for goods from Hong-Kong that could more easily have
been shipped by the Chinese river Sikiang. The British, whose
professed policy was "the open door to commerce", were
keeping a suspicious eye on the French colonies. They scented
competition for the Indian trade. It consoled them that up to
the present Tongking was costing France more than it was
worth. Officials proliferated there. In Haiphong, the port of
the Red river, three hundred out of eight hundred French
citizens were in the French Customs. But they were not
men of the stamp of the British botanising consuls and Dr.
Henry. They had little interest in the country's natural products. Indigo, cinnamon and cassia passed through their
hands without arousing their curiosity.

The journey was pleasant as far as Haiphong, afterwards,
less so. Henry travelled with a party of Customs staff; the Chief
Commissioner, Mr. Spinney and his wife; another Assistant
Commissioner called McCallum, and some Chinese. Henry
had known the Spinneys already in Formosa and liked them
very much. They were simple, decent, small-town Americans,
people who could be brave without knowing it, as a matter of
course. McCallum was a darker horse. He too had been in
Formosa, and in the confusion before the Japanese came he had
been helping on the republican revolution, and had apparently
done well out of it. The Customs evidently could not afford to
enquire too closely into the credentials of candidates for its
tougher assignments. He was a good man in a tight place.

From Haiphong they went on to Hanoi, the capital of
Tongking. Both towns had attractions. They were prettily
laid out with boulevards of flowering trees and an air of French
artistic taste. From Hanoi they were sent on in launches up the
Red river to Lao kai, a frontier fort. The launches were
crowded with French soldiers. Henry and McCallum slept on
deck in the rain. The soldiers sang. Two of them had good
voices. Friendship was cemented with a little brandy. They
were polite but dirty and uncared for. "Poor wretches," said
Henry, "so far away from *la belle France!*"[83]

The river really was red. Just as Henry had seen, on his first
coming to China, the mud of the Yangtze washed out to sea,

so now he had his introduction to the dark red clay deposit that covers the Yunnan and extends into upper Burma, the soil of the most fascinating flora in Asia. At this level the vegetation was tropical. It was bananas all the way. It seemed a rich country, full of possibilities.

There were rapids above Lao kai, and the party was transferred to junks with haulers, as on the Yangtze, to push on upstream through wild country for another seven days. This was where, as Henry put it to Evelyn Gleeson, for roughing it the journey surpassed his experience and his expectations. The boatmen's "rudeness, inefficiency and general hellery surpasses belief. McCallum and I, however, the first day out fought our crew with strong language and a few blows and got them thoroughly cowed. They worked hard, it is true, in the rapids, and all our belongings have come safely; but I am extremely sorry we didn't kill a few of them." This is Henry in a new light! "I think their conduct was due to perhaps the fact that possibly they were squeezed by the authorities (Chinese) and chiefly to their being *opium smokers* and old pirates. Mrs. Spinney behaved like a trump throughout."[84] There was also a Chinese lady and her attendant, but Mrs. Spinney was the first white woman to make the journey.

This was not the end. They arrived at "a village of ague and squalor" where two hundred mules were waiting to take them across the mountains, with sedan chairs for the ladies carried by coolies. The muleteers were like the boatmen, equally obstinate and stupid. They landed the travellers at dusk in a shed on the mountainside, without their bedding. Henry had luckily kept back a mule carrying food and wine. After an uncomfortable night they finished the climb, which went up to seven thousand feet, and then descended two thousand five hundred feet to Meng-tsz.

It was a small, old, walled Chinese city, set in about twenty miles of plain ringed round by mountains. Outside the city were two compounds with houses and gardens: the Customs and the French Consulate. There were no other European settlements. The land all round was bare of trees, as with all Chinese cities, but the jungle was not far off. On the way Henry caught a glimpse of two or three little dark men dressed in kilts. They were forest dwellers, not Chinese, and were shy of strangers. On arrival at the Customs compound they were shown a panther which one of the staff had shot just outside the gates the day before.

Within the city walls ten thousand Chinese lived herded in squalor. There was plague there. The newcomers were told it always broke out at this time of year. It would kill a thousand people and peter out at the end of August.

The Customs staff were very busy at first, taking over from the men they had been sent to relieve. When these left, society would indeed be limited. The Westerners were faced with the problem of getting on with each other. In the outposts one met stupid men with no future elsewhere, or clever men who were social misfits. Henry's predecessor, Hancock, had done some botanising and left him a list to work on. Henry wrote of him to Evelyn Gleeson: "He is the queerest fish out, very clever and talks twice as much as I do, but with a queer temper and curious ways. There is also a little French doctor here, who is sensitive, good-hearted, nervous and foolish."[85] Another man was "given to narcotics, excitable by temperament, with a clever but ill-balanced mind. He is, I think, the most foolish person I know and the least suited to this lonely life."[86] A complicating factor was the French national suspicion of the British. Even the Customs staff were suspected of being British agents. If they and the staff of the French consulate got on each other's nerves it could spark off an international crisis. Protocol, therefore, was strictly observed. Diplomatic calls were exchanged as punctiliously as in Peking, and further intercourse embarked on only with caution.

As for the Chinese, Henry told Professor Sargent: "It is pitiful to see the class of ignorant officials who are stationed on this southern frontier, where the presence of France in Tongking and England in Burma would, one might think, stir the Chinese to have intelligent officers."[87]

The Spinneys represented the real forces of civilisation. Mrs. Spinney, the first white woman to set foot in Meng-tsz, at once set to to organise her existence in the style to which she was accustomed in Salem, Mass. She had her whole house done up, with each room painted a different colour. The dining-room was a rich terra cotta. Her house was as well furnished as any London flat. She actually imported a piano. It took twenty coolies six weeks to carry it forty miles over the mountains. When it came the Spinneys gave a little dinner to the French consul, his assistant, the doctor and Henry. They introduced a new card game, a sort of converse of whist, called "hearts". Henry found Mrs. Spinney had not yet seen anything of the country, she had been much too busy.

Henry had made for the mountains at the first opportunity, and there, in the pure air and lovely surroundings he at last began to shake off his sense of guilt and loss. The novelty of everything, plants, birds, animals and the native inhabitants, gave him back his zest for life. Armed with a blackthorn stick from Ireland, he went for a long tramp every Sunday. On one of his first walks he almost trod on a panther. "He crawled away slowly and lay down twenty yards off under a bush. I had a good view of him for ten minutes. I walked away in the opposite direction, *not* throwing a stone at him as my insane coolie suggested."[88] The commonest bird was the gay, crested hoopoe. Even the snakes were pretty, and Henry was sorry when the coolies killed two that got into his bedroom. He had changed from the youth who shot game around I-chang. He no longer wanted to kill things, merely to observe them. He sent for a camera.

Most interesting of all were the native tribes. There were at least three distinct races in the mountains. Some were tall and handsome; others small and ugly, but gay and always laughing. In one place they wore hemp clothes like sacking, in another they were dressed in long, dark-blue garments, rather like Blue-coat boys. The littlest people had the most elaborate clothes; short trousers or skirts and heavily embroidered jackets, with caps like smoking caps, or turbans with silver ornaments. Seeing a party of them trooping all together, home from some festival, Henry thought of Irish fairy tales, and wondered if these could have had their origin in some prehistoric pygmy race.

These were the ancient owners of the country, whom the Chinese had dispossessed. Nobody knew much about them. Protestant and Catholic missionaries were trying to approach them, but nobody knew what they worshipped. They had no idols. There were said to be annual assemblies under certain trees. They fascinated Henry, and by degrees he got nearer to them.

In the plain round Meng-tsz he saw their women working in the watery rice fields, bare-legged, some with children on their backs, some holding up a huge umbrella with one hand and working with the other. They affected to be shy, but he noted with amusement that they adjusted their turbans as he approached. "The universal feminine question," he told Evelyn Gleeson, "Is my hat straight?"[89]

He met a party on the road and asked them what people they were. The only reply they would give was that they were "Large-footed people". It was meant as a jibe at the Chinese custom of binding women's feet.

The small, ugly, gay people were the Pu-la or the Miao-tsz, who came of a dwarf negritto stock scattered across the Pacific as far as the Andaman Islands. The taller, more dignified, good-looking people were Lolos, and their ways were mysterious. They preserved the remnants of former culture, and possessed manuscripts in a different kind of writing from Chinese. The races had intermarried and there were many individuals who were a blend of them all, but the racial groups were still distinct, and lived in strange isolation. Villages three miles apart might know nothing of each other.

The Chinese themselves were strange enough. "We had a very dry time till a few days ago and every device that superstition could suggest was put in force to bring down the rain. . . . We had daily processions, sometimes of ordinary folks, sometimes of the elders all marching with banners and tom-toms and chanting hymns to the gods, and all with their hair hanging down their backs. The south gate of the city is still closed, an expedient deemed very efficacious to cause rain. The slaughter of all animals was forbidden and the market was held outside the city."[90]

Evelyn Gleeson and Mary Henry could not imagine their sociable friend in this remote place. They commiserated with him, but he reassured them. He would rather be there than anywhere else in China. "I positively enjoy myself in the wild luxury of beautiful air, in the beautiful loneliness of our mountains, in the freedom from contact with commonplace people. I shall probably go on content here for two years at least."[91]

The first rapture faded. Rain came. It spoilt his first long

collecting trip. He slept in inns where the best accommodation
was the cowshed, and passed through one village which sickened
him with its dirt, where all the inhabitants were diseased. The
mails were delayed by the weather, and after a month without
news from home he suffered from "aridity of soul".

He and Mr. Spinney had an unsavoury affair on their hands.
A European on the Customs staff had loosed off a gun in
trigger-happy fashion and killed two women of the aborigines.
They made the killer resign, and the case was hushed up for
money, as most things could be in China, but it left a stink in
the air. The corruptibility of the Chinese magistrates was so
notorious that in the wilds men took the law into their own
hands. Homicide was easier to get away with than theft. News
came in that a horse thief, caught by some muleteers, had had
his sinews cut and then been burnt to death.

The frontier region had hardly yet been explored, but it
had been written up, by Henry's *bête noire* Colquhoun. The
British government kept an eye on it. There was an outcry in
the British Press because the Chinese had handed over a British
province to the French. According to Henry the "province"
was forty miles of barren hills with a population of a thousand,
and it was handed over by the mistake of a Chinese official.
Nevertheless, the British demanded and got reparations.[92]

Presently Britain and France both sent commercial missions
to South Yunnan. In January there arrived in Meng-tsz a
Monsieur Rabaud and a Monsieur Vial, who had come up
from Burma through the Shan states. They were "nice chaps, no
chauvinism". Monsieur Rabaud in dark blue pongee silk set a
high standard of elegance for the wilds. Henry had long talks
with them and learnt more about the country, and bought two
ponies from them for an extended journey.

"We will be the two ponies, four pack mules, the dog, old
Ho (a trusted Chinese collector), the boy and the coolie and
myself. The Chinese authorities don't guarantee any protection in these native states; but I anticipate that I can get on
very well without their protection, relying on a certain even-
ness of temper and of demeanour."[93] He took a camp-bed of
French make which rolled up and weighed twenty pounds, and
an American folding table and chair. "I don't know how I have
got on heretofore without such articles. I generally used temple

altars as my table."[94] He set out in rather a lukewarm spirit, feeling it was his duty to explore while he had the chance. It turned out a great success and a tonic.

"Glorious trip—high mountains, 9,000–10,000 ft., densely wooded, enormous trees, beautiful camellias, rhododendrons, magnolias. Large deer, great bears. Military reception in the native states, three guns, guard of soldiers. Two brothers (like those in Gondoliers) reigning, pleasant chaps, kind, dinner on Chinese New Year's Day with them, guides provided, etc., etc. Seven distinct races of aborigines, peculiar dresses, customs, different languages. Collected vocabularies of their words, etc. Found Lolo writing still in use and secured a small specimen of it. More to be done about aborigines in future."[95]

One other man had studied the Lolo language, a French priest, Father Vial. (He does not appear to have been any relation to Monsieur Vial.) He was highly secretive about his researches, was said to want the whole field to himself. Henry thought there was room for him too. He set about enquiring for a teacher, through the friendly native chiefs. No aborigines had ever been employed by foreigners at Meng-tsz, and in China it is difficult to do anything unprecedented. Henry wasted an amount of fair words and promises on likely subjects, but in May he finally succeeded in engaging a Pu-la of Lolo stock who had an aunt living in the town. This boy took him to see his friends and relations in a jungle village. They were poor but not miserable, and their family life seemed to him more natural and affectionate than that of the Chinese.

Henry's interest in the aborigines did not interfere with his plant collections. To deal adequately with these would require another book. The plants of the South Yunnan were not, on the whole, such as would grow in the open in England. But for botanists the whole region had a twofold interest. It appeared to be the place where many kinds of plants originated, and its flora had been left undisturbed. Knowledge of this flora explained much that till then had been obscure in the distribution of species.

Henry nowadays made up his specimens in seven sets of duplicates for distribution to various institutions. As well as pressing, sorting and labelling them, he had to solve the problem of preserving them from insects and from the humidity of the climate, which had destroyed a collection of Delavay's. He obtained from America an apparatus for poisoning plants by carbon bisulphide.

He corresponded regularly with Sargent, whose first interest was trees; with Thiselton-Dyer, who was being distracted from China by the economic possibilities of South African products; and with a new client, A. K. Bulley, the founder of Bees Ltd. He was a great patron of plant collecting, who afterwards employed both Forrest and Kingdon-Ward. He was "a bit of a Fabian, who wants to introduce beautiful plants to the cottages of the poor."[96] Henry sent him orchids and seeds of many kinds.

His letters were sprinkled with mentions of finds to make a gardener's mouth water: a large pink lily, a honeysuckle with flowers seven inches long, a gorgeous paulownia, rhododendrons, begonias, magnolias. He was falling more in love with the look of flowers, thinking less of their economic uses. His tastes, however, were not quite those of the average gardener:

"I like plants with beautiful foliage and neat little flowers," he told Evelyn Gleeson. "I don't care for colour much. I think chrysanthemums are positively ugly on account of their wretched leaves. The rose is an exception; it is wonderfully beautiful in every way. As for geraniums, I really can't understand anyone liking them. Ferns of all kinds please me. They are simply marvellous here, especially the kinds that one gets in the virgin forests."[97]

In the solitudes he had time to formulate opinions on many matters. He had, for instance, critisicms to make of the missionaries, in writing to Evelyn Gleeson, a fellow-Catholic. Even within their Church the variety of interpretations of Christianity was confusing. Spanish Catholics in Formosa and French Catholics in the Yunnan differed greatly in their approach. The mission stations in the wilds were of great assistance to explorers, yet by dint of this they became in spite of themselves the spearheads of political encroachment. In more civilised places the missionaries could be a great nuisance to officials by their interference in social problems. Their intervention on behalf of converts in the Chinese law courts

1. Augustine Henry
by Celia Harrison,
from the original in
the Henry Herbarium
at Glasnevin.
The foliage is
*Rhododendron
augustinii.*

2. Alice (Elsie) Henry
on the left, with
Miss F. Geoghegan,
a great Irish gardener.

3. Henry in China, looking every inch an anti-hero.

4. Evelyn Gleeson, his regular correspondent (second from right), with a family party at Benown House, Athlone.

was particularly resented. There was an element of "Souper-ism" about many conversions which caused the converts to be very unpopular with the non-Christian Chinese.

Henry found the ordinary Chinese perfectly reliable: "I myself never lock things up and am honestly served."[98] Yet, according to him, "The Catholic missionaries scarcely ever trust their converts and they never love them, so far as I have seen. There are very few Chinese priests, and they can't be trusted in money matters; if they have a parish their priesthood is to them a sort of official position by which they can 'squeeze' money out of the parishioners."[99]

His observations of the influence of various religions in China gave him no confidence in any of them as factors in the progress of humanity. Mohammedanism, Buddhism, Brahman-ism, each had some good points, yet their general tendency was to debase. As for Christianity, "The Great Unknown knows the harm even that has caused. You see all these re-ligions make right living a *puzzle*; you have to believe in one thing, to do another. Puzzles are bad to live by."[100]

He instances the preaching of celibacy, which flies in the face of natural evolutionary law. All Henry's thought was coloured by the theory of evolution, which he had imbibed in his most impressionable years. *The Origin of Species* had been published when he was two years old. The storm over it had died down and the concept of natural selection dominated every scientific field. As a botanist he sought reasons for every established variation: "I am much interested in the devices plants have for getting their seeds to a distance,"[101] and he encloses for Evelyn Gleeson several different pods, some split and jerk their seeds out; others have winged ends, and are blown to a distance; sometimes the seed, not the pod, is winged. "It is very curious to note how even European weeds seem to be prepotent and vigorous. They are ousting native weeds in many parts of the world,"[102] is another typical observation. Applying the operation of natural selection to human beings, he could write this:

"It does seem absurd that so much should be made of an epidemic of plague. I quite admit that sanitary regulations will do much to abate it. But if people don't want to be sanitary, I don't want to press them very hard, as there are

F

other and more *vital* things to be taken into account. It is a great problem how to deal with the enormous mass of superstition, ignorance and prejudice embodied in the 600,000,000 people of India and China. European rule and influence brings peace and trade and prosperity; but great increase of population. In ancient times things were always mended by wholesale destruction by war and pestilence and famine. China is very ignorantly spoken of as an ancient country of peace, etc. It has never been without rebellions, awful in their destructiveness."[103]

Thus even a humane European came to regard the millions of Chinese as expendable. Henry was more troubled by the cutting down of forests and the extermination of animals. There were elephants in the jungles to the south, but they were relentlessly hunted for the ivory—to make, as Henry said, billiard balls and paper knives. Another market was for deer's horns. A business man offered fifteen pounds a set.

It would be false, however, to suggest that he was consistent in the more extreme views he uttered from time to time. He had condemned the Socialist Party for its materialism, yet he liked to see people's lot improve: "One reflection comes from seeing different peoples in different stages of civilization. People who are brought up Catholics are apt to think too little of material progress. Yet it is the greatest blessing, the only evil in which the best virtues can grow. And to *intellect* we owe everything, I mean intellect applied to practical affairs, to science, to road making, to cleanliness and health."[104] "Prosperity is good, but it would be bad if it came (which is improbable) in the Socialist way, by throttling individuality. The Socialists, however, do good by pointing out blatant evils."[105]

One conclusion he came to, in which reason was at one with sentiment, was that free choice in marriage was essentially to the good. Arranged marriages interfered with the workings of natural selection. Romantic love matches were nature's way of bettering the human race.

News of the outside world trickled through to Meng-tsz fairly steadily, though the mails ran many hazards. The camera Henry had sent for arrived waterlogged, having been dropped into a river. Barrels of wine for outlying mission stations were often found to be empty. Illustrated papers were apt to be stolen by the French postal officials—"though how modest English pictures can interest them I don't know".[106] But the principal English and American papers did get there, usually about two months late. There is mention of *Harper's Magazine, The Nation, The Saturday Review, The Fortnightly, The Spectator, The Review of Reviews, The Academy, The Sketch,* Labouchere's *Truth,* as well as *The Times* and the new *Daily Mail.*

One of Evelyn Gleeson's letters at last contained some news of Miss Townshend, though only in the way of gossip. Henry's own correspondence with this lady had ceased. He was afraid he might inadvertently have offended her. She was still on his mind. On June 7, 1897, he had a dream of her, a vivid impression that she was in some kind of trouble and that he was powerless to help. He had noted the date, vaguely wondering if there was any telepathy involved, though his scientific training inclined him to dismiss such an idea. Then came the letter mentioning that Evelyn Gleeson had heard Miss Townshend was getting mixed up in the activities of the Fabian Society, and the more extreme and highbrow Socialists, the Webbs, the younger Phillimores and Bernard Shaw.

In his reply we see Henry bringing all his common sense to bear on this: "I had a very bad time of it for a few hours after your account of Miss T., i.e., to say I was despondent. In re-reading your account of her danger I am somewhat reassured, because the account derived by you from Mrs. Brownlow was perhaps obtained by her from someone else; and there are marks in the story of a dramatic and anti-Socialist mental bias; so it may not be true. I dislike Socialism immensely, because, as I have explained, it is a sort of inverted worship of Mammon, but I don't imagine Socialists are in a conspiracy to injure Miss T. I hope she will escape all machinations of evil—but you may be too late, so hurry, hurry and get to know her. Is there not a better field for her energies in work like yours and the Pioneers'?"[107]

Whatever the truth of whatever Miss Gleeson had heard, and whether or not there was any telepathy in Henry's dream, Miss Townshend must have been in some mental turmoil. She was making her first break with her family traditions by entering boldly into the politics of the left, and furthermore she was

getting to know Shaw quite as well as she had known Axel
Munthe. Although she had kept two of Henry's letters, perhaps she had not read them very attentively. They did
not prevent her from rushing on her fate, which was not so very
dreadful after all. A year later, Henry saw the notice of her
marriage in a paper, and soon after had a letter from Evelyn
Gleeson, intended to break it gently. Again he brought common sense to bear. He wrote back: "Everyone seems to agree
that he (Shaw) is honest. That is a main point. I am not
grieved to hear of her marriage, I am pleased. She will, I think,
be happy."[108] He visited the Shaws when he got back to
London and was satisfied that his prediction had been fulfilled.

Another item of news from London about this time was the
arrival of the "new woman" at Kew. Thiselton-Dyer had two
now training in the gardens. They wore knickerbockers and
were rated as "boys".

Whether or not it was due to the report of the Lyons Mission,
the development of the frontier region was being accelerated.
The French had begun to build a road from Lao-kai to
Meng-tsz. In June a new French consul arrived, and with him
a mining engineer. A new Customs post was opened at Ho-
kow, across the river from Lao-kai. This was the former headquarters of a bandit chief who had decamped to Formosa when
the French took over, and for whom McCallum had run a
Customs post during the attempt to set up a republic. The
remnants of this ruffian's band still troubled the Ho-kow area.
McCallum had made his own profit out of the Formosa
business. It now seemed highly fitting that he was sent to take
charge at Ho-kow. Mr. Spinney also had to go over there for a
time, leaving Henry in his place at Meng-tsz.

During the time when he was thus tied to the office, Henry
received an invitation to attend a Lolo wedding. It was hard to
have to refuse, and the opportunity never came again. But he
did see a lot more of the Lolos. He was on the brink of further
adventures. For he in his turn was appointed to another new
Customs station, at Szemao, several days' journey to the west.
This took him right into the country of the aborigines. It was
the strangest of all his journeys.

Before leaving he sent off thirty-two cases of botanical specimens.

8

The journey to Szemao took eighteen days, for Henry travelled in state. He had a caravan of forty mules, the leaders bedecked with flags. The muleteers were civil and helpful and everything went without a hitch.

With him went "old Ho", the Chinese collector (a Meng-tsz man), and old Ho's wife. The latter rode astride a pony, dressed in her best, and added to the picturesqueness of the caravan, but Henry was grieved to observe the cool neglect with which a Chinese woman was treated in the inns, and etiquette forbade him to address a word to her himself. There was also a little dog called Lo-mi, a parting gift from Henry's Lolo friends. It sat on a box of silver and caused great amusement to children along the way.

The weather was fine and the country "was more like a fairy panorama than an affair of real life".[109] They passed through immense forests, climbed high mountains and descended by precipitous ravines to rivers crossed by suspension bridges. Henry had heard of these bridges, how alarmingly they shook in the wind, but he found them better than he expected, very well made "of iron rods joined by rings at the ends, the best specimens I have seen of Chinese blacksmith's work."[110] There were good specimens too of Chinese architecture; pagodas, temples and bridges. The road connected three or four large Chinese cities. Along it moved caravans of tea and silk and cotton. Here an age-old social system was in being, yet nature over vast areas was still uncontaminated. The woods were full of wild life, birds sang and sometimes they heard the barking of deer.

The cities, the inns, the road itself were Chinese; the country was still the home of a variety of native people. And all the country folk were out along the roads. Henry had come at a lucky time. It was the Chinese New Year, when the government remitted a tax on salt, and everyone went to the mines to buy it when it was cheap.

To the south lay the Shan states, politically dependent on China, since the British had not claimed them on taking Burma. North of the Red river the people were mainly Lolo, and south of it mainly Shan, but there were also the Wo-ni, the Yao, the Kadoo, the Akas and the Kawas. The Kawas were "noted for scantiness of clothing and bloodthirstiness of disposition."[111] The Yao were seldom seen, but at the crossing of the Papien river Henry met five hunters who made a pleasing impression on him, "so trim, so neat, with very handsome guns and clothes and winning, agreeable manners".[112] The Shans were "given to gorgeous gowns and much dressing of the hair".[113]

At one place he was shown a Lolo sacred tree. Beneath it was a sacrificial table for dog's flesh, and from the branches hung an egg—unexplained—and a toy ladder "for the descent of the thunder god".[114] The Lolos were the most fascinating of all the tribes. Their looks and manners were prepossessing, their ways ancient and mysterious. To crown Henry's pleasure in the journey, he fell in with a Lolo wise man, one who could read and owned some manuscripts, and he persuaded this man to come with him to Szemao.

His arrival was no anti-climax. He was accorded an official reception. Three detachments of soldiers were sent to escort him into the town. He rode in a sedan chair with four bearers. Flags waved, guns were let off, crackers exploded, and the whole procession was timed by two boys beating gongs. It was hard for the representative of the Imperial Customs to keep his gravity.

The Customs quarters had been an inn. They had paper windows and low doorways on which Henry kept bumping his head. His own rooms looked out across a little court with flowers to a market square with a tree in the middle. There was a cross wing with apartments for his two assistants, Mr. Carey and Mr. Williams, and a labyrinth of servants' quarters at the back. There was a dark room with three official cameras. In front of the building were lanterns "as big as a hamper",[115] a row of spears carrying flags, and "two wooden collars for evil-doers".[116]

Henry had a reception room furnished in Chinese fashion, with a place on the left of the host for an honoured guest. He

decorated it with bunches of peacock feathers. The whole
place had been fitted up by his predecessor, the first official in
the job, an American called Carl. Mr. Carl had provided a
good supply of crockery and cutlery, glasses and cocktail
shakers and a quantity of tinned food. Henry paid his official
calls in a green sedan chair preceded by a servant to announce
him. He found himself in for an orgy of entertaining.

He was not the only new arrival. There was a French consul,
replacing the last one, and a British one come to open a new
consulate. They had all travelled separately to avoid over-
crowding the inns. Szemao had never seen so many foreign
dignitaries all at once. And as if there was not already excitement enough, the local Prefect had just died, so there were the
funeral ceremonies.

Henry sent the dead man's family, on behalf of the Customs,
a large tray of food and a six-foot square of red silk bearing a
message of sympathy. In return he received, according to
convention, a piece of pale blue silk to wrap round his
head at the funeral. He and the acting-Prefect led the procession
together.

"We walked at the head of the gentry and officials, all
dressed in their robes. The son of the deceased, dressed in sack-
cloth and howling piteously, supported by two servants, walked
or staggered along in front of the coffin. The scrolls with
laudatory epithets were carried on poles in front, and there
were two or three people with hideous masks, and others dressed
in tiger skins who lent an element of grotesqueness. The ladies of
the family came behind in chairs, all howling dismally."[117]

The acting-Prefect was a nice old gentleman. "He had
quakerish and honourable ideas and was noted for his freedom
from money-grasping."[118] He gave an official dinner to the
foreigners, and strongly advised them to marry. The girls of
the Shan tribes, more lax than the Chinese, were quite prepared to contract unions which would automatically be dis-
solved on the departure of the man. The Prefect thought it
helped to avoid scandal. But Henry was no Pinkerton. He
found the idea distasteful, however much it might have assisted
him in studying the aborigines. "Such sacrifices to science are
not in my line."[119]

The next social event was at the British consulate; the

hoisting of the first Union Jack to fly in the Yunnan. There were toasts: the Flag, and the Army. The army was represented by a youthful lieutenant, a guest of the consul's, on his way back to an Indian regiment. He made a speech. Mr. Carey of the Customs played the banjo, "and we sang 'Wrap me up in my tarpaulin jacket', 'Clementine' and 'The Wearing of the Green' ".[120]

The outgoing French consul was missed. He had made a study of the aborigines and collected some manuscripts. When he and the young lieutenant and Mr. Carl of the Customs had all departed only five Europeans remained. Jamieson, the British consul, was the one Henry found most congenial. He was an intellectual man with an original outlook, but neurotic and "full of pungent dislikes".[121] M. Sainson, the French consul, was a good man, fond of reading and animals, but invalidish and not a good mixer. Henry's two assistants were both English. Williams was about his own age, ex-navy, and a placid type: "He enjoys a good appetite and has three music boxes and smokes a number of cigars every day and doesn't want anything more.'[122] Carey was young and more inclined to be pushful. He was the son of a Wiltshire farmer, not very well educated but with a talent for drawing. It was he who had shot the panther at Meng-tsz the day before Henry arrived there. He had some contact with Lord Curzon (soon to be Viceroy of India), and sent him accounts of Chinese affairs.

Henry was now Acting Chief Commissioner of Customs. His salary had been increased, but he found it quite hard to maintain the dignity of his position on it, for he was paid in silver, now worth only two-fifths of its face value. A great part of his duties was routine office work "of the same calibre as is required of a clerk in a merchant's office".[123] Nevertheless, he was the Emperor's representative in Szemao, with status as a mandarin. The Prefect made much of him with dinners and presents, which Henry had to return. No doubt he had an expense account; he probably also had strict ideas of what should go on it. Dinner jackets were *de rigueur* in the jungle. Henry ruefully told Evelyn Gleeson that his had gone mouldy in the rains and would only pass muster by candlelight.

The community into which this handful of working Westerners had been dumped was at much the same stage of development as a city state of Europe in the Middle Ages, in the days of robber barons. Not long before, a local Shan chief who had killed a Chinese colonel had been invited to dinner in Szemao and executed at the dinner table. "This is a usual Chinese way, as they don't seem to have the Arab idea of the rights of hospitality. The common people here wonder why we are not slaughtered some day when we are at dinner with the Prefect."[124]

Henry had to buy some land on which to build a proper Customs house. The obligation was on the seller to clear out tenants, and one family refused to go. Finding an eviction in progress, Henry investigated the trouble. "The people only wanted ten dollars to clear, so I had the proprietor round and the tenant and arranged the matter, satisfactorily I think, so that the evicted now have the ten dollars to spend at New Year and establish themselves in a new home. The rascally proprietor, a rich man, had surreptitiously employed a Yamen-runner (the official servant of the Prefect) to frighten the poor people; and this made me angry; still I have thought it best not to take notice of this irregularity, as after all the proprietor was only doing what all the rich Chinese do—trying to oppress the poor with threats of the officials. These Yamen-runners in China behave in a way too horrible—when they get a man into their clutches he is privately tortured and made to pay large sums of money. Every Chinese official Yamen is a hell on earth. Yet our Prefect here is a humane man, and while he must know of these doings he apparently can't stop them."[125]

Henry's letters of this time contain a good many reflections on the British Empire, varying somewhat in tone according to whether his correspondent is Evelyn Gleeson or Thiselton-Dyer. What he writes to his Irish friend is in the nature of an apologia. He praises the British officials in general (who, he admitted, were mostly Irish or Scottish). "Responsibility begets even in the hastiest-tempered good qualities of firmness, justness, coolness, and the British officer is *good* all the time."[126] If Meng-tsz had been under British rule the burning of the horse thief could not have occurred. "In fact, the English flag means in all eastern countries the destruction of so many degraded and awful tyrannies, and the hells cease. . . . I do not like the extension of empire; I do not glory in it, but it is a stern necessity. I can only accept it as a solemn duty, an irksome duty. It is hard work governing an alien race when the native instruments are so corrupt."[127]

To Thiselton-Dyer he wrote, when he first learnt of his appointment to Szemao: "I am very pleased to get within the zone of British influence, and hope to see on some trip the beloved Red-coats who are in scattered posts in the upper Shan states, and of course some of the officers may come across to see us."[128] But the nearest British outpost was fifteen days journey away, and after the consul's young friend left, the only British army visitor in the year and a half of Henry's stay was an eccentric who wore Chinese dress with a monocle, ate Chinese food, smoked Chinese tobacco and did not want to go home on leave because he had a Shan wife.

The connection of Szemao with the outside world was "so slight as to be scarcely noticeable".[129] There was a telegraph line. It ran through the jungles of Laos and was often broken by wild elephants or storms. Mails came every ten days from Lao-kai, taking twelve days longer than at Meng-tsz. Trading caravans brought nothing of interest. "One or two of the *mighty* caravans Colquhoun speaks of came in the other day from Burma. They had some cheap cottons, umbrellas, pictures of the reigning sovereigns of Europe, pain-killer, quinine and such like. I don't think that Manchester need get excited."[130] Henry now had a new grievance against Colquhoun. He blamed his writings for the fact that a post had been opened in Szemao at all.

It was all the worse for him because he had more responsibility than at Meng-tsz and could not get much into the country. The collecting of plants went on, but it was mainly done by "old Ho". Henry missed his long days in the mountain air. The climate was healthy. There was no plague. But from the end of May till mid-September there was never a day without heavy rain. It was then that the five Europeans began to suffer badly from the monotony and isolation. Their minds felt atrophied. They recalled that Russian officers in similar stations in Siberia committed suicide at the rate of five per cent annually.

Sometimes they deliberately set themselves subjects of conversation. One day Henry and Jamieson set out for a walk together and gave it up because neither of them could think of anything to say.

Henry's old friend Joe Fisher, now a journalist in London, pressed him for copy. Couldn't he, for instance, describe the doings of an ordinary day? But living through it once was enough. Thiselton-Dyer put into the *Kew Bulletin* [131] a private letter that Henry had dashed off under the stimulus of that memorable eighteen-day journey from Meng-tsz. It touched, among other things, on politics, and Henry was disconcerted to find his views being quoted in other papers. It made him circumspect. He was inhibited by his scientific training from committing himself on any subject he had not examined in all its aspects. He did not want to lay himself open to the charge of superficiality which he brought against Colquhoun.

In wet weather and on days when he was tied to his quarters Henry studied the Lolo language with the teacher he had acquired on the journey. This man stayed two months. Before he left Henry had a good vocabulary and a general idea of the grammar, enough to enable him to go on reading with the help of any other literate Lolo he could get hold of.

The first detailed studies of this people[132] were published during the eighteen-nineties by the French Catholic Missions. They were the work of the French priest, already mentioned, Father Paul Vial. Notes on the Lolos had appeared in various British and French scientific journals. They were described in a British Blue Book of 1888 and given a chapter in a travel book of 1890 by the able and well-known British consul, Alexander Hosie. Henry was the first British student of their literature. In 1902 he read a paper on them to the British Association, afterwards printed in the 1903 *Journal of the Anthropological Institute of Great Britain*. He compiled a dictionary, the manuscript of which was thought by his widow to have been presented to an American institution. Efforts to trace it have failed. He never found time to write a book on the Lolos, and had to refuse an offer to conduct a scientific expedition to them. Like his study of the law, his plunge into anthropology was a step off the beaten track, but up what a fascinating by-way!

There are said to be about two hundred thousand Lolos in China, and some seventeen thousand scattered through Tongking and Laos. These latter are not the true Lolos. They belong to a lower caste descended from slaves of various races, who became absorbed into the Lolo people, and later on were freed and drifted south over the border in search of land. Henry's Lolos can only have had a small intermixture of Lolo blood. Some costumes he obtained from them, now in the Manchester Museum, turned out to be typical of another group, the Miao-tsze. But they spoke the Lolo language and observed Lolo customs, and their manuscripts had been handed down from ancient times. They do not seem to have minded parting with these. Henry sold about thirty to the British Museum in 1908.[133]

There were books of religious rituals, genealogies, old legends and songs. The writing had something in common with Syriac scripts. It was in pictorial characters arranged in columns, like Chinese, but the columns were read the opposite way, i.e., from left to right. Among their legends was a story of the flood, and they kept a sabbath every sixth day. Henry wondered if they had been influenced by the Nestorian Christians, a Syrian Sect who came to China in the seventh century A.D. and later were encountered by Marco Polo.

Their religion does not seem to have much in common with Christianity. Like most primitive peoples the Lolos were harried by the fear of ghosts and demons and spent a great deal of time propitiating or exorcising them. There were magic rituals for use in illness, and the rites of death went on for many days. They kept the spirits of their ancestors in boxes. Every village had a stone and a tree that were the centre of worship. They also had a kind of totemism; their surnames were derived from trees or animals, and to enquire a man's name meant asking, "What is the thing you do not touch?"

In a letter that appeared in the *Kew Bulletin* Henry noted: "The Lolos have a rigid enough set of morals; but they are entirely devoid, I think, of the idea of *sin*. They have the conception of wrongs, done by one person to another—infractions against tribal rules, etc.—but of sin in the individual, hurting the individual himself, there is no trace, I think. Nor can I find any idea of sin as an offence against spirits or gods."[134] His own Catholic training made him alive to such distinctions. He evidently reflected much on religious questions, though he did not practise observances.

In spite of their preoccupation with demons the Lolos of Yunnan were a gay people. Henry fancied they had a resemblance to the Irish: "They are strangely reminiscent of home in their bright, graceful manners, in their separate religion from their Chinese conquerors, in their poverty."[135] They kept secular feasts with music and dancing, and played games like tig and blind man's buff. The girls in the fields sang to the boys:

> "We girls three,
> The black earth's silver bridge,
> Together with you youths, we have crossed it;
> The white sky's golden hat,
> With you we have worn it;
> The golden fan of the sun and moon,
> Together we have seen it wave.
> We girls and boys tonight have met.
> Singing and playing comes from the hearts of
>   boys and girls;
> Silver comes from China;
> Silk from the capital;
> The rice from the plain;
> The wheat from the mountain;
> But courting-talk comes from the mouths
>   of boys."[136]

In 1901 the French established at Hanoi an *Ecole d'Extreme Orient* which became a centre for the study of all the tribes of Indo-China, and much work has since been done in this field. But the Lolos remain mysterious even yet.

Their true home is in the mountains enclosed by the great southward curve of the Yangtze, where it divides the Yunnan from Sze-Chwan. They have strongholds that can be reached only on foot, sometimes only by athletic feats. From these impregnable places they from time to time come out to raid Chinese towns. The ruling caste, the black Lolos, have strict marriage laws, which have kept them racially pure and distinct from the slave caste, or "white" Lolos. These "princes of the black bone" as Peter Goullart calls them, are dark-skinned, tall and aristocratic, with a strict code of honour among themselves, though they have savage feuds between clans, and are a terror to the Chinese on their borders.

Goullart, one of the few Europeans ever to have got inside the Lolo country, depicts a romantic landscape of woods and fields, where peasants go about their seasonal tasks, and lords and ladies, gaily dressed, ride out from their castles on parties of hunting or pleasure, as in the illustrations to mediaeval books of hours. He was entertained by some of these nobles, found them well bred and courteous to strangers, desirous only of keeping their independence, disdaining the outside world.

Lin Yueh-hua, a Chinese anthropologist from Harvard who visited them in 1943, lays more emphasis on their feuds and savagery, and the dirt of their dwellings. His account suggests that Goullart's is idealised. The Lolos still carry off Chinese and enslave them. These unfortunates are not exactly ill-treated, but they have a thin time and little hope of escape.

Most likely the Lolos are still resisting assimilation, and they must be a thorn in the side of the People's Republic. And perhaps the boys and girls, out of earshot of the radio, still sing about the black earth's silver bridge.

In the summer of 1897 there came good news. The salaries of the Customs men were at last to be brought in line with the rising cost of living. Henry's was doubled. He would now have £900 a year with free house, furniture and postage (the Customs had taken over the running of the postal service). In future he would be able to save, and he began to think that by 1900 he could afford to retire.

There was a new spirit in the air. It almost looked as if the much-talked-of awakening of China were really taking place. The old Empress and her favourites had faded into the background after the disastrous war with Japan. The young Emperor and his ministers were open to learn from foreigners and adopt some of their methods. The Imperial Customs started a school for Chinese diplomats and consuls. A high Chinese official went to London and St. Petersburgh to negotiate a foreign loan. There, too, the Customs could help. Its credit was good with all the western powers.

Some sweeping changes were made in the educational system on which the whole Chinese bureaucracy was based. They went too far, too fast, and provoked a reaction against the new movement. But the Emperor's worst mistake was a move in the old Chinese tradition. He tried to have the Dowager Empress's chief eunuch murdered. The plan was betrayed. The much more efficient Empress organised a *coup d'état*. From then on the Emperor was virtually a prisoner. The Empress had known how to bide her time. She had routed the reform party. But she was far too shrewd to antagonise the foreign ministers, and as a gesture of great condescension she invited the wives of all the ambassadors to tea.

Henry's salary was not affected by these changes. Nevertheless he viewed the course of events with dismay. He would have liked to see Britain support the party of reform. He had a poor opinion of the British Minister at Peking, knowing something about him from a friend who was his secretary. Gossip said he had got his appointment through making a hit with Lord Salisbury at a garden party. Henry told Evelyn Gleeson, "He is just as clever as and no cleverer than the average good-looking chap on Piccadilly."[137]

He wrote some sharp criticism of the British to Thiselton-Dyer. It was, he said, their failing, to pretend to act from high moral purpose. All the talk about "maintaining the integrity of China" and "the open door for commerce" did not disguise from the Chinese that they were as anxious to make profits as any other nation. In the East as in the West they were obsessed by the idea of the balance of power. In particular, he thought, they were foolish to be jealous of Germany. Germany was a competitor, but "we shall prosper by having rich neighbours".[138] Perhaps feeling he had gone too far, he ends: "The preceding criticisms don't abate by a jot my admiration for the many excellent qualities of the Englishman, which as an Irishman I can see so clearly. The Englishman is easily first in the world for justice, fair play and level-headedness."[139]

He wrote in the same strain to Sargent: "I am convinced that if an honest effort were made by such nations as the U.S. and England to help China to strength and independence, such an effort would have its effect. But the Chinese can see nothing in European nations but the conqueror and the spoiler, and with reason. The independence and good government of China by the Chinese is an object much more worthy of going to war about than your Cuban affair; and it is the *most* important question of the epoch. If things are allowed to drift, and China becomes an area for crooked diplomacy like Turkey has been for a century, it will be a bad thing for civilization."[140]

Henry was not alone in these views. Sir Robert Hart was saying the same kind of thing in more influential quarters. So were many men of goodwill, but not enough.

The murder of two German missionaries gave the Germans an excuse to seize the port of Kiao-Chow for a coaling station. The Russians countered by occupying Port Arthur and securing the right to build a railway in the north. The British, not to be outdone, obtained the lease of Wei-Hai-Wei, opposite Port Arthur, for a naval base.

As for the Chinese, more and more of them were enrolling themselves in anti-foreign societies. The Empress saw this without disapproval. Her ministers began to lend them a kind of countenance. China could not afford to maintain a large standing army. Sooner or later she might need troops. Where was the harm in encouraging what, from their point of view, amounted to a patriotic volunteer movement?

9

At Szemao the year 1898 melted peacefully into the year 1899. At Christmas the Chinese Prefect presented Henry with a goat, two fowls, a roasted piglet, oranges and some curious silver-ware—miniature cups, saucers, plates, spoons and forks, crudely made and quaintly decorated. Henry responded with champagne and Californian tinned fruits. For friends at home, he ordered China tea from a shop in Hong-Kong. He received ten Christmas cards, when he would much rather have had letters. He had all the five Europeans to Christmas dinner.

The end of the year was a busy time. In the office there were

5. Hauling junks up the Yangtze rapids, "there were times when as many as two hundred men were needed."

6. Military escort of the Customs Commissioner at Mengtze. *Both from photographs probably taken by Henry.*

7. At Lochinch Castle, near Stranraer. Henry (back turned, centre) is walking off, no doubt to inspect a tree.

8. Table made in the estate carpenter's shop at Colesbourne out of a cross-cut from the trunk of *Platanus orientalis*. It was Elwes's wedding present to the Henrys, and is now in the possession of Dr. T. J. Walsh.

statistics to compile and reports to write in Chinese and English. The Chinese New Year came a month later, and both New Years were occasions for exchanges of official visits.

One of the activities of the Customs was to promote interest in China's art and folk lore by contributing to great international exhibitions. There was one coming off in Paris. Mr. Carey went on a tour to buy things from the aborigines and secured the hat of an Aka woman, "a castle-like edifice of cowrie shells and silver".[141] Also the head-dress of the leading ox of a Shan caravan, a structure of shells surmounted by a peacock's tail. According to Henry, "the leading ox shows by his demeanour that he is very proud of his ornamentation."[142]

Jamieson, the British consul, was sent to act on a boundary commission appointed to fix the frontier between China and Burma. Henry missed him.

Henry received encouraging reports of his Meng-tsz collections. He wrote gleefully to Evelyn Gleeson: "I sent Mr. Dyer a lot of seeds and he gave them to the girl gardeners to grow, and these dears succeeded in raising 45 kinds (already) including six specimens of begonia, and a new species of rodgersia, etc., etc."[143] A Swiss botanist[144] published a paper on some of his Meng-tsz ferns, which included sixty new species and two new genera. "New genera," Henry explained, "are missing links as it were, and very delightful to the spectacled enthusiasts at home."[145]

The flora at Szemao was similar to that at Meng-tsz, yet distinct from it. There were different species of the same genera. "Old Ho" was still doing most of the collecting. The plants he brought in revealed great possibilities, and indicated where it would be most worth while to go. It was not till February, 1899, that Henry himself went any distance from the town of Szemao. Then he had some official business that took him off on a two-week journey.

He was shocked to see the rate at which the country was being deforested. He had already suggested to Thiselton-Dyer that Kew should send out a professional collector. He wrote now that it was urgent. Everything indicated that this region was the central point from which a flora had spread over Asia. It would soon be too late to investigate. In fifty years many plants would have become extinct. But Thiselton-Dyer was

G

very busy with African vegetable products, and in any case
Kew had no funds to finance expeditions.

Henry wrote also to Sargent of Harvard, and Sargent was
interested. In his next letter Henry worked out his idea in
detail. First it was important to find the right man. He had
in mind someone like himself in his younger days, who would
work for the love of the task as much as for money, but he must
be better qualified; if possible an all-round naturalist. He
need not necessarily know Chinese; it was not as if he was
coming to study commerce or folk lore, he only had to get
himself to the habitats of the plants. Transactions like
the purchase of goods and the hire of coolies could be carried out
through an interpreter. One such man would be all he needed
in the way of a servant. He could be engaged at Shanghai or
Hankow, and must understand "mandarin", as the dialects of
the coast towns were no use in the interior.

Chungking or Yunnan-fu would be suitable starting points.
There the explorer would plan his route in consultation with
European residents, and hire men and mules. The expenses of
travel would be small if he took advice from old hands. There
was no necessity to spend large sums like the foolish type of
globe-trotter.

He calculated the expenses in round figures, which would
only be of academic interest now. The main headings were:

    1. Salary.
    2. Fare to Shanghai.
    3. Hotel expenses at Shanghai and fare to Chungking.
    4. Running expenses of expedition to the interior:
        (a) Wages of interpreter
        (b) Six coolies to carry baggage
        (c) Ten coolies to help collect and carry
            collections
        (d) Food, inn expenses, etc.
    5. Expenses of return journey to Shanghai including
        freight on collections.
    6. Return fare from Shanghai.

To this he added, "Of course the procedure is very rough,
and the coolies required for transport will depend on the nature

of the collection aimed at. I presume that no attempt would be made to transport live plants in Wardian cases, and that the collection would be of (1) dried plants, say four sets, (2) seeds and bulbs. Boxes, paper for drying plants, etc., can be procured cheaply in the interior. A coolie will carry about 60 lb. A mule will carry 120 lb. Wages of coolies about six dollars Mexican a month; hire of mules about twelve dollars Mexican a month. Inn and food expenses very trifling indeed."[146]

One mule was apparently the equivalent of two coolies. Such was travel in the interior of China in the year 1899.

Sargent wanted Henry to lead the expedition himself. Henry was tempted. A few years earlier he would have jumped at the chance. Now he weighed the matter. Sargent wrote more than once to urge it. He offered to pay the equivalent of what Henry earned in the Customs, which Henry said was "preposterous" for a collector. It was not a question of money.

So many new Customs posts had just been opened that the Service was temporarily understaffed. Henry did not like to apply for special leave, such as had been granted him years before at I-chang. He had been treated with consideration at the time of his wife's illness, and he had a sense of obligation towards his employers.

He might perhaps have sounded Sir Robert Hart on the matter if it had been easier to communicate with Peking. But there had been more anti-foreign rioting, messages sometimes went astray. It was not the time to raise personal problems.

These were sufficient reasons for refusing, but as he honestly admitted to Sargent, they were not his only ones. He did not much want to take on the responsibility for an expedition, "for the spending of other people's money".[147] He preferred to regard botany as a private hobby, not a job.

Moreover, to take up plant collecting as a profession meant committing himself to stay many years more in the wilds. He had lately begun to build on the prospect of early retirement. His letters to Evelyn Gleeson are full of plans for his return to London or Ireland, one might almost say his return to life. "I have lost the zest of youth and am in fact *tired* of China, mentally dead tired of it."[148] Exploration was a job for a younger man.

A younger man was found, though not by Sargent. Thiselton-Dyer had succeeded in interesting James Veitch & Sons, Ltd., of Chelsea, an old-established nursery of great enterprise. They sent out a Kew-trained collector. This was E. H. Wilson. He travelled out to China and came straight to Henry. Henry showed him the ropes and shed on him, as it were, the mantle of Elijah. In later years Wilson collected for Sargent, and became in the end his successor as head of the Arnold Arboretum at Harvard.

There was news of serious rioting in the district round Chungking. Henry's friends the Archie Littles lived there, but were now in England. In Hupeh, at a place where Henry had botanised, a hundred Chinese Christians and a French priest were massacred. A report came that Consul Jamieson and his party had been murdered, but this turned out to be false. The mails were much delayed. A paper dated December 28th arrived at the end of March.

Henry had not encountered any demonstrations in the course of his official journey, and at Szemao everyone was friendly. The Prefect's nephew came to him for English lessons. Henry liked this "young dandy of twenty".[149] As he said, it gave him the opportunity to study young China. "Indeed I am rather sympathetic with the Chinese at present, as the country is in a distressful way, and the barefaced attempts of foreign countries to seize the empire and divide it have no sympathy from me. I advocate protectorates and letting the people rule themselves with the minimum of foreign interference."[150] Nevertheless he concludes, "stern necessity conquers all, and I am afraid England will have to rule more of the world than ever".[151]

It was not easy to think straight, especially when the rains began and the skies were leaden and the atmosphere humid. His friend Jamieson came back safe, but only to leave again for a new post. He had a good deal to tell of the task of administering Burma.

"If the experience of the British in Upper Burma and its pacification were told plainly, all of it, I don't think people would be as fond of foreign conquests. There is a tremendous amount of killing to be done—i.e., all the warlike chaps and plucky fellows and bravados, etc., amongst the natives have to be got rid of; then you can govern satisfactorily afterwards."[152]

"We are all thinking of that great problem the 'white man's burthen' and it is by no means the plain sailing that it looks in Kipling's poem. There is another side to the question. There is an incompatibility between democracy and the extension of empire, and big armies, navies and hosts of autocratic officials do not go well with that peaceful progress and development of the social life of the average man which one wishes for in the future."[153]

The French were suspicious of Henry's relations with his Chinese pupil. It seemed to them a Machiavellian way of spreading British influence.

In May there happened a sad thing unconnected with politics. Henry's trusted collector "Old Ho" died of malaria while on a botanising excursion. Only a week or two earlier Henry had remarked in a letter on the susceptibility of the Chinese to this disease, which had kept them from penetrating into Annam and Burma. "Old Ho" died by the roadside. His companions could not persuade anyone to take the body in and had to leave it till Henry could send out a party from Szemao. He had it grandly coffined, an important matter in China. "I wish I could write a fitting account of him," he told Evelyn Gleeson. "He was an exceptional Chinese."[154]

It was a month after "Old Ho's" death, and while Henry was awaiting the arrival of E. H. Wilson, that the anti-foreign discontent, so long a threat on the horizon, suddenly broke out at Meng-tsz. The news reached Szemao in a vague and garbled telegraph message. The Prefect and the Europeans thought best to keep it from the public. There was a long delay before the courier arrived with further details. The delay was due only to the weather; the rains were heavy that year, rivers were in flood and bridges down. But the interval was an anxious time. The Europeans went on doggedly with their jobs, not knowing if they might not be the next to be attacked.

A mob had broken into the Customs compound at Meng-tsz at night, but all the foreigners were safe. Both the Spinneys had shown great presence of mind. Mr. Spinney had evacuated the staff under fire and they had taken refuge in the walled town. Two Chinese coolies had been killed and the buildings had been looted and burnt. Had it not been for the coolness of the Spinneys many more lives might have been lost.

The trouble was not, after all, political. The border mountains between China, Annam and Burma were the refuge of outlaws of all kinds. The Chinese authorities had not enough police or soldiers to put them down. After the riot they made an effort to round up the ringleaders. Some were seized and beheaded, others fled further into the mountains, and some into the neighbourhood of Szemao. There a leading bandit with a dozen adherents held out for some time against three hundred Chinese soldiers.

They killed him in the end and brought back his head in triumph to the blowing of trumpets and exploding of fire crackers. The head with two others was hung on the tree in the market square, opposite Henry's window. There was great rejoicing among the common people, who had gone in fear of the bandits for years. Henry did not think there would be any more trouble, though he kept a revolver handy. He wrote to Sargent that this kind of thing need not put a stop to exploration. "There are always lots of places where quietness reigns."[155]

E. H. Wilson had actually arrived at Lao-kai while the riot was taking place at Meng-tsz. Had he come a week earlier he would probably have been killed on his way over the mountains. He was proceeding on his way to Szemào for the sole purpose of meeting Henry. His instructions were not to waste too much time on this sub-tropical country but to move on to the more temperate region round I-chang.

The prospect of Wilson's arrival spurred Henry on. Through July and August all his Sundays were devoted to botanising in spite of unceasing rain. This is how he conducted these last excursions:

"I ride to the ground, take three coolies along, one carries a bill hook, another a box in which collected species are put and a basket containing the materials for a cup or two of tea and a tiny luncheon which is always the same, eggs, leg of a fowl, bread and butter and bananas. I never take tobacco on such trips and I have a horror of alcohol when taking exercise. In fact, when I reach England, I shall be practically a teetotaller. The third man leads the pony when necessary. It is very exhausting for the coolies as on arriving on the ground we have much hard work in the jungle."[156]

He never ceased to marvel at the tropical forests. "Here every form of vegetation is to be met with. The tall trees, the small trees that grow in the shade, the climbers that, too weak themselves, depend on the trees for support to reach the sky. In the gullies and ravines grow the tall ferns and graceful palms, with here and there great grasses twenty or more feet high. On the trees the orchids get a foothold, and besides them the smaller and pretty ferns. . . . There is one marked peculiarity here about many trees and climbers. The flowers are not borne on the circumference with the leaves but low down on the stem where leaves are absent. They are meant to take advantage of the lower stratum of the forest where such flowers can be seen just as well as if they were on top on the sky line."[157]

He was falling more and more under the spell of trees. He hated to see them wantonly destroyed. "The necessity which will always exist for timber will necessitate in future great forest reservations, so there is hope. A forest is the finest thing in the world."[158]

Yet the possibility of making forestry his career did not occur to him when he thought about the future. He found it hard to imagine what he would do, or where he would live. In one letter he says, "I could hardly live in Ireland, as the peculiar feelings there of religion, politics, etc., would only amuse or annoy me and I couldn't take sides,"[159] and in the next, "So London, in your opinion, is decidedly the place to live. I suppose I must agree, but smaller places have a fascination. . . . It is not fair for all the clever nice people to concentrate on London. I often think some sweetness and light ought to be bestowed on the provinces. I recollect well the narrow life of a little Irish town, how stupid it was, as it could easily have been brightened up. If it weren't for theology and bigotry and politics, life would be so much pleasanter in such places."[160] Many an Irish emigrant might say "Amen" to this.

The foreign community at Szemao wined and dined to celebrate the French national day in July, and shortly afterwards the Empress of China's birthday. Henry and Mr. Carey packed up a hundred and fifty-four objects for the Paris Exhibition and labelled them all in French.

In October, at long last, E. H. Wilson arrived. He had been detained for weeks at Lao-kai. He was not quite what Henry had expected. He had hoped for a university man, but Wilson had only his Kew training behind him. In other respects he was well qualified for his task. He had the prime requisites, common sense, tact and good temper. He spoke no Chinese, but he got on well with the local people. Henry foresaw that he would do excellent work, and his expectations were fulfilled.

Hardly had he arrived when they were both obliged to set out again. A telegram came appointing Henry to take charge at Meng-tsz.

It was promotion and a short step nearer home. Yet he did not leave Szemao without some regret. There is always sadness in such a final farewell. The Chinese Prefect sent him off with honour. The road was lined with soldiers and banners, and the old gentleman himself and his nephew, Henry's pupil, escorted him for ten miles on his way.

Of all the Chinese Henry had known, these two were the nearest to being real friends. Yet it was a friendship within limitations. "I doubt if they ever gained an idea from me or I from them." "The gulf between East and West is immeasurable," Henry wrote to Evelyn Gleeson. "It is never spanned. I doubt if the missionaries even ever get to be friends with their converts who are Chinese. The Chinese are set hard in their own fashion and detest us Europeans, as people they don't understand, and as people who are really their enemies, who come to rob them of their country."[161] It was a sad conclusion reached after so many years of working in and for China.

10

The weather made the journey back laborious, otherwise the party had no trouble. They collected plants along the way.

Henry secured some more Lolo manuscripts and saw a Lolo place of worship, a stone in a grove of oak trees.

They met the caravan of Mr. Litton, who was to replace Jamieson at Szemao. He was an Old Etonian. Henry had met him in Shanghai and thought him "rather a cool customer, not exactly my type", but after some hours' talk in these wilds he came to like him much better. Two months later he was shocked to learn of his death in a frontier ambush.

After eighteen days of heavy going through tropical rainstorms they reached Meng-tsz to find the Customs buildings still in ruins. Till the Spinneys left and Henry moved into their quarters he had only one small room to himself. The cases of his collections were dumped on the verandah. A guard of sixty Chinese soldiers was encamped in front of the ruins. They were all opium smokers and slept most of the time.

Things sorted themselves out by degrees. E. H. Wilson took charge of Henry's specimens. He was going back to Shanghai via Hong-Kong, and then up the Yangtze, and undertook to send them off from the coast. That was a weight off Henry's mind. The weather improved at last. The country seemed to be pacified. The Chinese authorities were civil and made arrangements to build Henry a house.

Meng-tsz was livelier than it had been before. It was swarming with French engineers and soldiers, employed on a survey for a new railway from Lao-kai. The military were charming people, of the politest French army type, and the consul was a decent, peace-loving man. Two Frenchmen had also been added to the Customs staff, one of them a nice Breton lad of twenty-two whom Henry took for botanical walks.

All at first seemed well. Nevertheless, the coming year was to be the most arduous of all Henry's official career.

There were undercurrents of local feeling which it did not take long to sense. The French railway was a symbol of foreign encroachment that inevitably provoked resentment. Henry did not see much of the French; they were a world of their own. The ordinary Chinese, however, tended to lump them all together as foreigners. They had another grievance in the compensation they had to pay for the damage to the Customs house. This was a matter between the local authorities and the Imperial government, but the blame, naturally, fell on the foreigners.

Things were going from bad to worse in China. There was bad news too from the outer world. It was one of those dark periods when all human events seem to be wrongly guided. In October 1899 the South African War began. It caused grave heart-searching in those who were already aware of the price of empire. Evelyn Gleeson asked Henry for his opinion.

The year before, when America was fighting Spain to secure the independence of Cuba (and improve conditions there for American business), Henry had met the arguments of pacifist friends with the concept of man as a fighting animal. He could talk then about a righteous war, point cheerfully to the prospect of promotion for those who fought, and see it as all part of the process of evolution.[162]

Now, he had not his answer quite so pat: "I think with good management and statesmanship it could have been avoided and I blame Chamberlain. One's opinion of all such events is coloured by the fact that English rule is really the best in the world and its extension must make for civilisation. I am very sorry though that a brave, if ignorant and obstinate people must be slaughtered to extend that rule. The Boers, however, will be the better of a little fighting; and I hope peace will soon be attained . . . I haven't thought it out."[163]

Stewart Crum, the husband of his sister Mary, was in the fighting forces. They had not been married much over a year.

The anti-foreign agitation all over China had become focused in the movement called the Boxers, literally "the Society of Patriotic Harmonious Fists". China had many such more-or-less secret societies, working in an atmosphere of mystification and magic. This one claimed to confer on its initiates supernatural immunity from being killed, as well as other strange powers. The Empress herself seems to have believed its claims. It was praised in Chinese official newspapers, and some high officials became members. By the end of 1899 the Boxers were drilling openly.

Sargent had gone on pressing the idea of the botanical expedition to be led by Henry. In November the latter wrote: "At the moment my duties are onerous, i.e., here we are sleeping with an armed guard on our verandah and a constant expectation (quite unfounded I believe) of another attack, for no one has the faintest belief in the power or ability of the Chinese authorities to keep the peace. They have sown the seeds of rebellion and distrust amidst the people, and their want of courage, moral or physical is incredible. I couldn't, however, think of going away from here now, as one must really do one's duty, especially as the Peking government has doubled our salaries and behaved so liberally. It seems to me that it would be a little unseemly to resign at the moment."[164]

In January he did actually frame a letter of resignation, which he never sent in. In another year his leave would be due and he could depart from China with honour. Even if it had not been against his instincts to desert his post it would have been against his financial interests. But his position was becoming increasingly difficult.

As already stated, it is unlikely that the trouble the summer before at Meng-tsz had any connection with the Boxer movement. Henry's difficulties had to be laid at the door of the French.

The French were concerned at the unprofitableness of their Indo-Chinese colonies. In 1896 a new governor, M. Doumer, had been appointed to Tongking, and had set out to improve its trade with China and step up its development. The new railway was part of this programme.

Among the less legitimate ways of extending influence is the sending of *agents provocateurs*, to stir up trouble, which you can then march in to suppress. In April 1900 there came to Meng-tsz a French official whose behaviour was so high-handed that Henry suspected him of playing this part.

He omitted to call on Henry, the Commissioner of Customs, as he should have done in accordance with protocol. Henry could not, therefore, call on him, and instead of being able to talk his complaints over, he was compelled to deal with the affair on paper. Long dispatches were exchanged, and copies of the correspondence, in English and Chinese, were forwarded to Peking. Henry had no doubts about the correctness of his own procedure. His letters do not say what particular points were at issue. There was an outcry over them in the Tongking newspapers, and some petty retaliation by interference with goods in transit through French territory.

To calm things down, Henry suggested to his superiors that they should transfer him to another post and appoint in his place one of the French members of the Customs Service. He was ready, like any good civil servant, to "take the rap". No reply came to this. In May, however, the high official (he was a consul-general) moved on to the capital of the Yunnan. Everyone was thankful to be rid of him, the *entente cordiale* was restored, and Henry and the regular French consul went for long walks on Sundays.

Presently word came that the consul-general had taken with him a lot of guns and ammunition, which were discovered by the Chinese. There was great excitement in Yunnan-fu. The official visitor and the missionaries were under protection, but the mob was out for their lives. This did not make things any easier for the foreigners at Meng-tsz.

The Boxers now were on the march. An army of them was moving in the direction of Peking, attacking missions and railways. The attitude of the Imperial government to this was ambiguous. The Ministers in the various legations asked permission to bring in for their own protection small parties of marines from the ships at Port Arthur and Wei-Hai-Wei. This was rather grudgingly granted.

At the beginning of June, ordinary dullness still reigned at Meng-tsz. Henry was in a fatalistic mood. His actions were all prescribed by routine and precedent, and all he could do was to keep calm and carry on. "I am besieged with annoying questions that crop up nearly every day. I am, however, rather used to them now, and take my difficulties somewhat philosophically. I am not in the least alarmed at the possibility of disturbance, as if it comes, it can't be helped, and there is always a good chance of getting out of it scot free."[165]

But the situation altered to one in which decisions had to be taken. The mission at Yunnan-fu was burnt. The consul-general was practically a prisoner. The French began to consider withdrawing from Meng-tsz. Henry had to decide whether, if they went, the Customs should go too.

There was risk both in staying and going. The authorities in Tongking could not send reinforcements to Meng-tsz without permission from the Chinese, who were not in the mood to grant it. If they invaded without permission, the whole party at Meng-tsz would be killed before help could arrive. If the French left, the party of twenty or thirty soldiers and officials with two or three refugee missionaries, would quite likely be attacked in the course of its retreat. If the Customs people went with the French they would be identified with their unpopularity. If Henry and his staff stayed (they were only five), they would be an embarrassment to the Chinese authorities and a source of provocation to the mob. It was doubtful if even the Chinese authorities would discriminate between foreigners if fighting actually began.

Henry's sympathies were with the Chinese, but the balance of safety, meagre as it was, seemed to lie on the side of joining the party of French. They for their part were awaiting instructions from the consul-general, if and when he should return.

Henry referred to his superiors at Peking for instructions, but there was still no word from the capital. Communication was by now cut off. Early in June the Boxer army had reached the outskirts of the city. The Imperial government gave permission to foreign Ministers to send for more troops to the ships. But this rescue party had to fight its way in from the coast. The Boxers had broken into Peking. The whole foreign community, Europeans, Americans, Japanese, including Sir Robert Hart and the Customs officials, were penned up in the Legation quarter, where they stood siege from mid-June to mid-August. They had four hundred marines to help in their defence. The Imperial government appeared to be powerless.

The question for Henry now became whether he could leave his post without permission. The lives of the Europeans under him could not be sacrificed to a moral scruple. He considered sending them away and remaining alone, but it would have been an empty gesture, and he was not indulging in false heroics.

In a series of letters to Evelyn Gleeson he seems to be thinking out the problem on paper, neither minimising nor magnifying the dangers. He sent messages through her to his sister Mary, and his wife's relations. On June 24th he wrote to them all, saying that matters were coming to a head. The French were almost certainly leaving. No one knew if the foreigners in Peking were alive or dead. Those at Meng-tsz took turns to stand guard at night, not depending on the Chinese. Yet everything was strangely calm.

"I have long since got past the worrying stage. We cannot realize here that there is any possible danger, though reasoning points that way. Everything around is quiet, the women are in the rice fields, in the mud up to the knees transplanting, and the country people carry into the market as usual firewood and rice. The hereditary chief, whom I visited three years ago, is here with 400 Lolos and Wonis as a guard against riot. My Lolo teacher is one of his clansmen and is turning out rather intelligent and interesting. I have now made out a syllabary of all the sounds to my satisfaction, the great difficulty being in a series of vowel sounds. . . ."[166]

He did get word from Shanghai. He was advised by the Customs officials there to leave Meng-tsz if the French did.

According to Henry, the French consul and army officers agreed with him in pinning the responsibility for the local trouble on the behaviour of the consul-general. He was on good terms with them. The danger had given a fillip to social intercourse. "We are all tolerably gay and dine as usual. The situation is so grave that it begets calmness; events are beyond human control, apparently—and that being the case one can only hope for the best."[167]

Evelyn Gleeson, meanwhile, was facing danger of another kind. She had just undergone a major operation. Henry's next two letters express his deep concern for her. In the second he says that the French are now definitely about to evacuate.

"I have done my best for peace by trying to interfere but with no result. I have nothing to reproach myself with. I reproach the French Consul-General Françon whom I brand as a fire-brand, selfish, vain and irresponsible. His government will know the real facts when too late. He cares nothing for the evil results of his pig-headed policy."[168] This letter reads as if it was addressed to posterity.

The Customs party did accompany the French, and they were not attacked. Henry transferred the books of the Meng-tsz office to Ho-kow, the former bandit stronghold across the river from Lao-kai. It was a squalid, fever-ridden hole. There he had to stay, marking time, for several months.

When the physical danger was over, nervous reaction set in, and was accentuated by uncertainty about the future.

The French papers in Tongking chose at this time to run a campaign of abuse against the English in general, the Protestant missionaries, and Henry. Henry reflected that this unpleasantness might have been avoided, and perhaps Meng-tsz need never have been evacuated, if notice had been taken of his request to be replaced by a Frenchman, the previous spring. His conscience was clear. Nevertheless, as it might seem to his superiors in their wisdom that he had blundered, he felt bound to tender his resignation. He intended in any case to resign, but it was one thing to depart with honour at the end of the eighteen months' leave on half pay to which he was entitled, and another to forgo six or seven hundred pounds and leave under a cloud.

It was three months before any reply came from headquarters. Meanwhile, he spent his days from ten to four in the Customs office at Ho-kow, with very little to do, and his evenings in the military club at Lao-kai, watching the French officers play manilla.

One evening an odd little comedy was enacted. "I dined pot-luck with the Commandant and there were present besides myself the French priest who is chaplain here and a missionary who has just come down from Yunnan. The latter is the only one except myself who has studied Lolo. He is an excitable, intelligent person, and the fun of it to me was that I believe he is the man who has been writing very abusive and incorrect letters to the Tongking papers concerning me and others. I heaped coals of fire on him, if so, as I was very amiable to him. Like a certain number of French he is absurdly anglophobe."[169] This, presumably, was Father Paul Vial.

Soldiers were being poured into Tongking. Many of those at Ho-kow died of fever. The mail steamers were for some time commandeered for troopships. Little by little communications were restored and news came in from other parts of China. One victim of a much-publicised Boxer atrocity was a missionary woman whom Henry remembered. He had sat next her at a dinner in Shanghai, and had advised her against going into the interior. Apart from her, none of his friends or acquaintances seems to have suffered. E. H. Wilson had all the time been peacefully collecting at I-chang, employing some of the Chinese whom Henry had trained ten years before.

The siege of the legations in Peking had ended on August 14th, when the troops from the coast got through. By that time the foreigners had been penned into half the Legation quarter, most of them in the large British Legation protected by a canal. The Belgian, Austrian, French and German Legations had all been shelled or burnt, also the American Methodist Mission, the Chinese Imperial Bank, the palace of a Chinese prince, which the defenders had taken over to house refugees, and the whole of the Customs buildings including Sir Robert Hart's own house. About sixty foreigners were killed and ninety wounded, out of five or six hundred.

The story has come down as a horror page of history. It was certainly a grim business for the besieged. The Imperial government had played a waiting game. Evidently the Empress more than half hoped this would be the end of the foreigners in China. Now she and her ministers and generals hastened to throw all the blame on the rebels, and helped to put down the remnants of the Boxers. But they could not hope to escape reprisals. In the fighting the Summer Palace, where the Empress had stored so many art treasures at so great a cost, was sacked and looted. An international force, sent to restore order, perpetrated atrocities to match those of the Chinese. The Germans had instructions to "behave like huns",[170] the Russians, at Amur, flung five thousand men, women and children into the river to drown. Large scale reparations were exacted. Henry told Sargent: "The honest, peaceable Chinese, who in the centre and south kept the peace, are mulcted in a heavy indemnity, which will put on heavy taxation to pay the foreign powers, who allow the treacherous and cruel officials (chiefly *Manchus*) to escape *scot-free*—these will gun down their own people, stir up hatred against foreigners, etc."[171]

As for Sir Robert Hart, he had been invited during the siege to mess at the British ambassador's house but had declined, and insisted on sharing the rations and hardships of his junior assistants. He was then sixty-five. His home had been destroyed. No sooner was he established in safety than he set to work to put the Chinese side of the case, in a series of articles, *These from the Land of Sinim*, published in book form in England in 1901. The first sentence is: "No one can say we were not warned. . . ."

The Customs went on with its work. Sir Robert retired with honour in 1908. The Service itself survived the fall of the Manchu dynasty. At its greatest strength, about 1910, it employed 17,700 Chinese and 1,468 foreigners drawn from some two dozen nations. Its policy was gradually to replace foreigners by Chinese. In 1949, when the Nationalist government gave way to the People's Republic, it had on its staff about 200 foreigners and over 10,000 Chinese. The foreign staff were pensioned off by the Nationalist government. A Chinese staff continues to operate in Formosa. Nothing is known about the organisation on the mainland, but it seems likely that the old Imperial Chinese Maritime Customs will have provided the new regime with the nucleus of an efficient contemporary service.[172]

At the beginning of December Henry learnt at long last that his resignation was not accepted. More, his advice was being taken. An assistant-commissioner had been appointed, not French but Italian, the next best thing. Henry had authority to hand over to him and go on leave till September 1902.

Mr. Tiberii arrived. He was a first-rate man, a Chinese scholar, musician, sculptor and doctor of law, "one of the best of our office men".[173] It was a great comfort to have his company. Everything was now happening for the best. The news from home was of Evelyn Gleeson's recovery, and Mary's husband returning from the war.

But Henry wrote of his homecoming without elation. He had sunk into a depression that was slow to lift. It brought him to the verge of a nervous breakdown. He postponed his departure on various pretexts, as if he had not the energy to go. Then he caught fever, and once again was shipped off with a high temperature, to recover in Hong-Kong.

He left China on December 31, 1900, the last day, as he said, of the last year of the nineteenth century.

PART TWO

"Better fifty years of Europe than a cycle of Cathay."

Tennyson (*Locksley Hall*)

"It is very curious that I seem to have finished with life, i.e., I have no hope or aspiration or desire for the future. I can only see a dull monotony and a useless existence ahead."[174] 11 May, 1900.

"I think I can see a well-defined and unoccupied field of labour where I can work with satisfaction to myself and benefit to others."[175] 18 March, 1901.

"I am now in robust health and looking quite young, if oneself can be trusted to see oneself rightly in the glass—I look a little over thirty, with a good deal, however, of too much noble forehead."[176] 26 March, 1901.

Henry quickly recovered his health and spirits once he got out of China. He went home via India because his sister Mary and her husband were returning there after Stewart Crum's demobilisation and he could see them on his way. While waiting for them to arrive he had three weeks' holiday in Ceylon.

There he was delighted to meet M. Vial (who had been to Meng-tsz with the Lyons commercial mission, not the Lolo student) and his charming wife. They all three went sightseeing. They visited a camp of Boer prisoners of war, magnificent men like Texas ranchers, the older ones great Bible-readers. They were well treated but pining for liberty. Characteristically sampling the life of the island Henry went to a tea-planters' meeting, met there an Irish planter and went to stay with him. He knew something of tea. His discovery of a wild plant in China had caused a revision of theories on its origin.

He climbed Adam's Peak, the high mountain of Ceylon, making the ascent by night in order to see the famous effect of the shadow of the peak cast on the mist at sunrise. "The sunrise was *enchanting*, the most beautiful sight I have ever seen. I *wept*, the beauty of the scene was so affecting."[177] Nor could he leave without trying to catch a glimpse of the Vedda, the primitive inhabitants of the great forests in the eastern half of the island. He travelled with a native who talked a little English, on a cart drawn by "a trotting cow". They started at 2 a.m. Through the dark hours the way was illuminated by the fireflies, one on every leaf. They stopped at a temple on a plateau and descended by day through forests into a deep ravine to a small mission run by the Portuguese. The Vedda were seldom seen. About once a month they crept out of the forest and arranged on the ground the beeswax and honey which they wished to trade. The missionaries laid out small axes in exchange. There were half-castes who could sometimes persuade the shy people to come to the forest edge. Henry did see them. They were said to be the most primitive of all human races and still to live in trees. He doubted this, and thought they might be degraded from a higher standard.

After these adventures came the joyous reunion with the Crums. "Mary looks wonderfully well—in fact quite a beauty in one hat. The babe is exceedingly intelligent and will be an LL.D. by-and-by."[178] He spent a week or two on their coffee plantation in the Nilgiri hills. Then, in the highest spirits, he sailed for England.

A disappointment awaited him. Evelyn Gleeson, with whom he had shared so much of his recent life on paper, had to leave London soon after he returned. She had not fully recovered from her illness of the previous autumn, and was going to Dublin, where she was to undergo another operation. They had one brief, distracted meeting, complicated by Henry's luggage, which as usual included large cases of plant specimens. He pursued her with an apologetic letter, but he could not yet go himself to Ireland. London was to be his headquarters, the best vantage point from which to look round.

London was changing. Wood paving was replacing cobbles. There was much new building, by new methods. Iron girders made the framework of the new Ritz hotel. Longer tramlines made it possible to live further out in the suburbs. In the centre one could now get about by "Tube". There were electric taxis, though not yet motor ones. Bicycles were common. Henry lost no time in learning to ride one. He practised in Kew Gardens after hours.

He found lodgings near Kew. For the next year he was to spend much time there working on his own collections. His standing was unofficial, but he had his own room there, and evidently was *persona grata*. The work had to be its own reward, but it solved the problem of an immediate occupation, and it kept him in touch with the botanical world.

In particular, he met people connected with forestry. It seems this must have been the "well-defined and unoccupied field" he already had in mind. Soon after his return his enthusiasm for it was rekindled by some Americans, the Pinchots, who were bent on saving the United States from being deforested like China. They had stirred the U.S. government to action, had paid for the foundation of a department of forestry at Yale, and devoted an estate of their own to a summer school. But in England it was difficult to make a start. The only school of forestry anywhere in the British Isles was an offshoot of the Royal Indian Engineering College at Cooper's Hill. So for the time being he went no further in this direction. After the long years of exile he plunged eagerly into social life.

He poured out impressions in letters to Evelyn Gleeson, intended to cheer the invalid up. He walked about and talked to people, rejoicing in the ease of communication. "It is not really I who begin to talk, but there must be about me some sign that I am interested in my neighbours. A nice youngish man in the train today told me all about his garden, how clerks on 35s. a week live, etc. A mechanic returning to the Woolwich Arsenal after a holiday told me he had a glass eye as the result of an accident, and that he had a black Arabian donkey, it was a pet at the Arsenal and was taken very ill once because of the amount of sweets had been given it. Of course the Arabian donkey may all have been a romance, but the glass eye was real."[179]

He revelled in any kind of theatre, but not uncritically. He did not care for the perennial West End society drama, represented then by Pinero with such plays as *The Gay Lord Quex*. He felt the emotion and power in the performance of some Japanese actors, the same no doubt as those who made a lasting impression on Yeats. And he was delighted with Grossmith's burlesque of a drawing-room tenor singing a sentimental ballad.

He took two schoolboys on an outing; they were Miss Gleeson's nephew and a friend. They went to see model yachts on the Round pond, had lunch in a café, visited the Natural History Museum and the Tate Gallery, and then had tea, a full and educational day.

He went to the Pioneer Club. Some of its progressive members inveigled him into attending a meeting of another women's association where a paper against vivisection was read by a determined suffragist. There were twenty women and one man—Henry. He had promised to speak, and it was awkward, foɪ he was a man of his word. He declined to discuss the main subject, but took the speaker up on a minor point.

He dined at the Temple, and there caught sight of Joseph Chamberlain. "He is smaller and more insignificant than I thought, with a hard, hard face."[180] Chamberlain, as Colonial Secretary in Lord Salisbury's government, had been responsible for many things of which Henry disapproved. In earlier years, as a Radical, he had turned the parliamentary tide against the first Home Rule Bill.

He visited the Bernard Shaws. They were living then in Adelphi Terrace, in the upper part of a house occupied by the London School of Economics. They asked him to lunch, it lasted the whole afternoon. "Three hours of most interesting talk, chiefly done by Bernard Shaw."[181] "I was much amused by Bernard Shaw's bright, brilliant and prolonged conversation, yet I am not at all sure that they are on the right track. Is any one? But they are happy and that is much. Mrs. Shaw looked quite happy and seems to have found rest. She was in the days gone by a perturbed spirit indeed."[182]

Later he characterised Shaw to Thiselton-Dyer as "expedient"—a word he thought conveyed a subtler shade than "opportunist".[183] People like Thiselton-Dyer did not know what to make of Shaw. Fabianism had no appeal for Henry. The Shaws were very busy and he did not see much more of them. Two years later came the first production of *John Bull's Other Island*, Shaw's only play about Ireland. Henry's friends declared they recognised him as Larry Doyle. There is no

real resemblance apart from their both being returned wan-
derers, but that three-hour talk might have helped on the
germination of the idea.

Directly after this display of Fabian fireworks at Adelphi
Terrace, Henry had his first, though by no means last, experience of the hospitality of the Edwardian rich. He was
invited for a week-end to the home of the family of a man he
had known in China. Socially, it was an eye-opener.

"It is very difficult to describe without exaggeration the
richness and luxury of this home . . . I had a delightful room,
full of cabinets of silverware and other curios; and with some
beautiful engravings and an original drawing of Landseer's,
an 'old horse' which reminded one of a drawing of a pony by
Leech in *Punch* long ago. There are many wonderful pictures
in the house and two beautiful statues from Florence in the
hall."[184] A fellow guest was Colnaghi, the dealer, aged eighty
but very brisk, "an amusing old cuss".[185] He thought modern
art poor stuff as compared with the old.

"I tried to enjoy it all and did so fairly well, and made Mrs.
Clarke rather happy by my appreciation of her gardens and
pleasure grounds." Yet he felt uneasy. He could not help
making inapposite reflections. "It is like being in a little
special heaven on a short trip. How can the elect in Heaven
enjoy their happy state knowing the miseries of the poor
damned souls?"[186]

The days were spent going round gardens. There were
some great gardens in Sussex. They did not see those of William
Robinson or Gertrude Jekyll, but they visited Lady Farren in
whose demesne some rare ferns grew as luxuriantly as in China.
The Farrens had recently been obliged to close their gardens
to the public, owing to vandalism. Henry was sorry. He
hoped they might see their way to open them again, in a
limited way under supervision. It seemed a great deal of
ground to be reserved for the exclusive pleasure of one man.

Not that the rich were lacking in social conscience. Lady
Farren's husband, who was away, was one of the founders of the
Rowton Homes for working-class men. There was in the
village a good school, a charitable foundation, where three
hundred boys were "well taught and fairly well fed"[187] for
twenty pounds a year. Nobody was discontented. On Satur-

day evening at dinner time the village band came and played in the grounds.

"As Bernard Shaw says, the working classes are all conservatives, as they prefer to live on the gentry and rich tradespeople and are servile. One sees nothing but the worship, absolute worship, of the rich by the lower classes, who are occupying exactly the same position as the Chinese coolies do with us in China. It is very different from the free democratic life of the United States, different even from the life of Scotland. The South of England is indeed to me a strange country."[188]

This visit brought home to him his need for new clothes (could he still have been wearing the mouldy dinner jacket?). On his return he settled down to study a catalogue of the Civil Service Stores alternately with a large book Mrs. Shaw had lent him on the drink evil.

Shortly afterwards he ordered a new suit. There was the ordeal of being fitted. "I had a look at myself in two mirrors at the tailor's and I am more horribly bald than I imagined."[189] Apparently he bore some resemblance to Rudyard Kipling. He often had arguments about Kipling with worshippers of the poet of empire. Henry had mixed feelings about him. He disliked his bombast, but admired his drive. One lady at a party rounded on him and accused him of being the man himself. People found him hard to place. He was often taken for an American.

He felt unsettled. Idleness began to pall. Engagements multiplied, but the people he met were all acquaintances, not friends: "Express trains that fly past in the twilight."[190] He could never really accustom himself to loafing. By temperament and habit he was a worker. Drifting made him feel demoralised. Moreover, it cost something to be a spectator of the passing show. Living like this was more expensive than he had foreseen. Ultimately he would have to find means of adding to his income. But first he wanted to get his collections sorted out. If he once got that job off his hands he could give up his lodgings at Gunnersbury and find somewhere more central. Summer was the time for this work as there was a rule at Kew against working by artificial light.

Soon he was getting up at half-past five and working sometimes from six in the morning till six at night. He would take half-an-hour off for lunch and have tea brought on a tray. "Yesterday I went in the afternoon to Blackheath to Mr. Dawson's and stayed very late, missing my proper train so that I didn't get back here till 12.30. However, I got up this morning at 5.30. . . . The fern specimens alone were about 1,000, all requiring separate labels. Tomorrow my oaks, beeches, etc., will take me all day. The work I am doing is perfectly appalling; and it is the last of this kind of work I shall ever do. It is upsetting all my plans and preventing me from doing, e.g., my Essay on the Lolos."[191] But though he grumbled it was the atmosphere he thrived best in, and there were compensating pleasures.

"Sir Joseph Hooker, the venerable old botanist, came in yesterday. He told me my specimens are the best he works with, so nicely dried and so complete. He is 84 and is spending his time now over wild Balsams, of which more than 200 distinct species occur in China and India. Think of ringing the changes on leaf and flower that make 200 quite different wild balsams. Isn't it marvellous?"[192]

He dined with Professor Oliver, the man who had been so pleased with the first collection he had sent from I-chang. Oliver complimented him on his letters from the Yunnan, some of which had appeared in the *Kew Bulletin*. There was material for a book, if only he could get round to writing it.

There were so many tasks to which he might set his hand, yet none of them offered any clear prospect of a livelihood. Sometimes he wondered if after all he would be wise to go back to China. He was still officially on leave, but everything there seemed to be going from bad to worse. He totally disapproved of all the doings of the powers in Peking, and saw that for minor officials out on a limb of the decaying empire life could only become more difficult. China for him could only be the last resort.

Meanwhile, the idea he had vaguely formed of taking up forestry was nourished by various chance encounters. At Kew he fell in with Sir George King, formerly Superintendent of the Botanic Gardens of India, who told him how to go about it. The French and Germans were first in the field. On the continent of Europe forestry had been taken seriously for some three centuries. Sir George considered the best place to go for training was the French State School of Forestry at Nancy.

Henry also in these first weeks in London met the man who two years later turned up in the role of *deus ex machina*. H. J. Elwes, author of a classic monograph on *The Genus Lilium*, took the chair at a luncheon of the Royal Horticultural Society to which Henry was invited to speak on his Chinese lilies. Elwes was himself a great traveller. He had been through a forbidden pass into a part of Tibet previously visited by only one foreigner —Sir Joseph Hooker. His collections of birds, butterflies and plants had earned him the much coveted distinction of F.R.S., and he was one of the sixty-three holders of the Victoria Medal instituted by the Royal Horticultural Society in honour of the old Queen's Jubilee. He was as impressive in his person as his achievements, a huge and handsome man.

Elwes invited Henry to his home in Gloucestershire. The date, however, was not fixed, and neither of them suspected that they would have so much to do with each other in future.

12

Henry had thought he might be able to join Evelyn Gleeson while she was convalescing from her operation in the glens of Antrim, but his botanical work detained him in London and she returned there just before he set out. By this lucky chance we have letters to her describing all his feelings on his homecoming, and these reveal how Ireland regained its hold on him. He was not, after all, to become completely expatriated. From the time of this visit home he had no doubt about where he belonged.

There was a reconditioning process to be gone through. The first stage was his adjustment to the atmosphere of Belfast. His friend Joe Fisher had gone back there the year before, as editor of *The Northern Whig*. He was a bachelor, living with his mother and sister, and Henry spent the first few days with them.

Old friends are apt to be critical of each other, and in this case neither of the two was quite satisfied with the other as he had become. Joe was now a prominent citizen, bent on making the *Whig* an important paper, and Henry got the impression that in his friend's eyes he was a "heftless" individual, a bit too much of a rolling stone. "I must really go to Lhasa and get the gold medal of the Geographical Society in order to put myself square with Joe and his world."[193] No doubt the newspaper-man felt his friend might have made more of an effort to send him articles from the outposts. Joe himself had been to Finland and published a book on the country. Henry had read this in China and found it dull.

In Belfast there were two inescapable topics: politics and religion. Henry had never made up his mind where he stood on the burning Irish question of Home Rule. Joe was opposed to it. He was a Liberal Unionist. The party had split off from the Liberals some fifteen years earlier when Gladstone decided to support the first Home Rule Bill. In other respects it upheld Liberal ideas. It pressed for social reforms. Henry, having read his friend's arguments in favour of autonomy for Finland, thought him somewhat inconsistent. Evidently he found him hard to pin down. Evelyn Gleeson had enquired how Joe's mind was veering. Henry said he didn't know. "He probably won't let his mind veer. His talk with me was interesting, but we only skimmed round subjects."[194]

A recent book on Ireland which Henry read at the Fishers' turned out to be an attack on the Roman Catholic Church. Its effect on him was to revive old loyalties. He had passed through crises without the support of faith. In the weeks of strain at Meng-tsz he had written to Evelyn Gleeson, "What a comfort the good old religion was! But I am as hardened an agnostic soul as ever."[195] But in Belfast, that dour, pragmatic city, he felt the need of "some real faith, religious, social or other. Men skim round the dread mystery, will not touch it, hear it spoken. They pretend that material progress, money, games, are real things. Yet we all know better."[196] Towards the end of his stay, after he had been deep into the life of the countryside, he wrote that Catholicism was the saving of the people. "The Catholic Faith, as it is believed in Ireland, has preserved to the Irish a grace and a good that are wanted in the Pagan material world."[197]

The editor kept newspaper hours and could not spare much time to entertain his guest. Mrs. and Miss Fisher took Henry to visit old friends, and driving with them about the country he soon found himself falling under its spell. The weather was ideal. The sun shone through a blueish haze on prosperous golden corn and profligate yellow "benweeds" and equally they delighted his eye. The heather in bloom was a sight to beat anything in China. The air, after London, was delicious— barring a slight smell of flax retting in the pools, to which no Ulsterman would object. The poor countrywomen might be slatternly, but how marvellously transparent were their complexions, and how admirably their faces were framed by their shawls!

He was in the real country at Tyanee, and this was his real homecoming, to the house which his grandparents had built and his brother Tom now owned, where his initials and Mary's name in full are engraved on the glass of a window. It is a plain grey slate-roofed house on a side lane with a small grass plot in front and a small yard at the back. It is placed on a slight rise in country mainly flat and commands a good broad view of fields and sky. This is down-to-earth farm land. There is romantic scenery to the north-east in the glens of Antrim, and in the Sperrin mountains to the south-west. Here in east Antrim the aspect of nature is utilitarian.

Tom Henry was not simply the stay-at-home brother. At one time in his life he went out to New Zealand. He and Austin were rather alike in looks and had much in common. But Austin found him now deeply rooted in his own locality. He had married a charming girl from another old farming family and they had five small, chubby, healthy children. Tom was a civil engineer by profession, but he had many occupations: "He farms and does a little land-surveying, and as a handyman broken-down machinery of any kind comes his way. He is legal adviser, general conciliator and social regenerator of the whole countryside, and has a good name which is better than riches."[198]

Everything was going on exactly as it had always done.

Everyone was very busy on their own affairs. They welcomed
the wanderer, but a man cannot expect to be made as much of
in Ulster as in London. Already Joe Fisher had subtly reduced
Austin Henry in his own esteem. He felt more of a prodigal
than a hero.

"My brother Tom is even also my accuser, as he does his
duty so well and fits into the scheme of things so neatly."[199]

Yet he was at home again. On Sunday he went to Mass "and
heard the curate on the subject of the Angels, their creation and
names and attributes, a fairy tale of the most charming descrip-
tion. The churchyard on the hill with the green graves, the
quiet, peace-loving people, so refined in their poverty, the
ancient ceremonial all called to one's imagination and one
wished no change in the scene."[200]

The weather had been too fine to last. "Last night great
gales blew and gusts of heavy rains made wild the darkness.
Today the sun leaps out, now and then, of the great banks
of grey cloud which are surging through the sky."[201] Fortunately he was not dependent on the weather for occupation.
In his brother's house he was well placed for observing Irish
life.

The temptation to analyse was irresistible. Ireland is so
fascinating a country, so blessed by nature and small enough,
one would think, to be manageable. The Irish are not stupid
people. So why the sense of something lacking? He kept
trying to put his finger on this something. Like China, Ireland
seemed to need awakening.

"If people would look forwards and not be always glancing
backwards, things would change like magic."[202]

Things *were* changing. Driving over to Ballymena to be
measured for a brown tweed suit, Henry gave a lift to a Mr.
Keenan who turned out to be a forward-looking gentleman.
He was a Roman Catholic, a large farmer, a Justice of the
Peace and a member of the County Council. County Councils
had only been instituted the year before.

In that year, too, the British government had created a
Department of Agriculture for Ireland. To a great extent this
was thanks to the hard work of Sir Horace Plunkett. He was
the organiser in Ireland of the co-operative movement, following the great success in England of this economic and social

experiment. Henry had read of Sir Horace's activities in
newspapers which reached him at Szemao. He had approved
wholeheartedly, and had wondered if the movement could find
a niche for him. There had, of course, been teething troubles.
So far, the guidance of the co-operative movement had been in
the hands of a voluntary body, the Irish Agricultural Wholesale Society. The new Department of Agriculture was to give
it official assistance and backing.

Mr. Keenan took Henry to see one of the new co-operative
creameries. This he found exciting:

"A young man, late of Philadelphia (U.S.A.), exhibited
the whole process to me, to his own great delight and mine.
I was able (probably the first outsider he had met) to follow
his explanations concerning butyric and lactic fermentations,
tests for acidity and quantity of butter fat, and of course
I made numerous suggestions and plied him with questions
for an hour or more. Twenty years ago if one had predicted
that butter would have been made in this thoroughly
scientific way (there are *bacteria* imported in bottles from
Denmark once a month!!) one would have been put down as
a crank. The creamery is the most significant material object
in Ireland; it is a triumph of co-operation, of science; it is the
first of a series of arts which will transform the material
aspect of the country. The creamery is the newborn baby
which will become a giant."[203]

There were other signs of a new spirit in the air. Snobbery
seemed to be on the wane. Mr. Keenan told him that game
preservation, formerly the sole concern of landlords, was now
being taken in hand by gentry and farmers together. Other
kinds of sport were developing on democratic lines. But the
small shopping centre of Ballymena was much as Henry remembered it—full of drunks on market day.

He had originally meant to stay only a fortnight and then
go on to Glasgow to the annual meeting of the British Association. But an accident befell him which kept him a week longer
at his brother's and gave him more time to reflect on Irish
problems. To mark the culmination of his visit, he and Tom
Henry set out together on bicycles for a long ride in the Sperrin

mountains. Austin Henry, coasting too fast downhill, fell off on his face and was shaken and bruised and temporarily disfigured. He lay-up at Tyanee, re-reading old books—*Vanity Fair, Jane Eyre, Pride and Prejudice*—and "devising a scheme by which the social and material condition of the people can be improved, Home Rule if required be obtained, the nationality preserved, and Ireland placed in the front rank of nations."[204]

Priests often came to his brother's house. They varied in their outlook, but they were really of the people and lived on familiar terms with their flocks. While Henry was getting over his bicycle smash the local curate called accompanied by a young American priest on holiday. "Strange the difference between the two, the American optimist, cheerful, charitable, modern, liberal. The other, not exactly the reverse of these qualities, but still anchored in what I call antiquated ways, but very good and honest."[205] When he was again fit to appear in public, Henry took part in a symposium on current affairs in Ireland. The panel consisted of himself and his brother, the priest of a neighbouring parish, and a prominent layman of the latter's flock. The discussion took a practical turn, and Henry was requested to make enquiries in London about the market for cottage industries.

On leaving his brother's, Henry went to spend a few days with his sister Matilda, now Mrs. Kerley, in Dundalk. There he met a priest of a different stamp, sporting and efficient rather than intellectual. "He shoots and fishes and never reads a book. He has built a grand church in a poor mountain parish with money collected in America, Australia, England, Scotland, etc. He doesn't believe in Plunkett."[206] But according to Henry's observations the Catholic priests were doing a good job. He thought the Church as a whole in Ireland had a great opportunity, and that through its means the people could best be helped to help themselves.

Most of all, he thought, the Irish needed to be given confidence in themselves. He was proud of the rising reputations of Irish writers in London. The Irish Literary Society there was flourishing. In China he had read with interest of its activities. Evelyn Gleeson was on the committee. Yet he did think the poetry of Yeats and A. E. was a bit too airy-fairy. He

I

wished for writers to deal at first hand with the everyday life he
knew, to voice the thoughts of the farming and labouring
people. He wanted a literature to dignify present-day reality.
He did not, as an Irishman, feel at home in the Celtic twilight
of London drawing-rooms.

He knew there was something there to write about and that
it was being neglected. On his way back through Belfast he
found himself again involved in arguments, and by this time he
was clearer in his own mind. "I had a talk with Dr. Lindsay."
(A founder-member of the Ulster Liberal Unionist Association.) "It will take some convincing to move him and Joe
Fisher and others to see that they are *blind* to certain
truths, No. 1 being that they are grossly unfair to Celtic
Ireland."[207]

Yet somehow throughout his life he never put much faith in
political programmes. His instinct was that social regeneration
should come of the people themselves. "I am not converted to
nationalism, or Home Rule as it is held by Redmond & Co."
(the Irish party in the House of Commons), "but I have really
more sympathy with them than the others."[208] Politically,
that was as far as he would go.

All that winter in London Henry went on thinking about
Ireland, and his own future in connection with it. He now at
last was able to see a good deal of Evelyn Gleeson. She had
been joined by her widowed sister, Mrs. MacCormack, two
little nieces and a nephew. Their pleasant family circle was
open to him when he tired of his lonely lodgings.

The little MacCormack nieces were allowed to dress up in
the costumes Henry had brought from the Yunnan, though they
soon outgrew them (as we have seen, the clothes belonged to
the small-sized Miao-tsze group, not the true Lolos). They
also remember dancing with him an alleged Formosan dance, a
ferocious romp which reduced one little girl to tears. They
preferred being taken to the Zoo in a hansom and given ice-
cream.

With the help of these friends Henry moved from Gunnersbury to more central rooms in Southampton Row. Evelyn
lent him odds and ends of furniture, and took over from him
some of Caroline's pictures. London held many memories of

Caroline, and her friend was one of the few people to whom he could speak of her.

Evelyn Gleeson also enabled him to gain a first experience of lecturing. He had so far delivered only short, informal talks. She took the chair at a meeting of the Pioneer Club when he gave a lecture on the Lolos, which he was to repeat on many other occasions. Lecturing came more easily to him than journalism. He responded to the stimulus of a live audience. This new-found ability became a considerable asset.

London abounded in clubs and circles of enthusiasts. Henry described some of his friend's friends as "living far too isolated among brachycephalic peace people and black silk liberal women".[209] But he himself was far from despising groups ardent for good causes. He was quite a joiner. He and Evelyn Gleeson did not go so far as to follow W. B. Yeats and A. E. into Theosophical lodges, but they were faithful supporters of the Irish Literary Society, and they went to dances and Irish language classes organised by the Gaelic League. Henry at this stage took to beginning his letters "A cara", a salutation which has since become very familiar to those who have correspondence with the Irish Civil Service. Nowadays, when the Irish language gets, on the whole, rather a bad Press, it is touching to find how excited people could get about it in the year 1901. Henry wrote, adapting a passage of Turgenev:

"In the days when doubt, when anxious thoughts on the destiny of my country oppress me, thou alone art my stay and support, thou ancient, beautiful, true and free Irish tongue! Wert thou not, I must despair in the face of all that is done at home. But it is impossible that such a language should be conferred on any but a great people."[210]

An extra benefit, he said, was that copying the Irish alphabet improved one's handwriting. The improvement is not much apparent. The letters of this winter, of course, are mostly notes dashed off on matters which would now be communicated by telephone.

Henry's Irish friends were not very much interested in botany, nor his botanical friends in Ireland. One household that had links with both worlds was that of Dr. Hartog, later Professor of Botany at Cork. The Hartogs were Jewish, musical and artistic. At their house Henry met the novelist Israel Zangwill, a dark, intense young man solely interested in his work.

Some time during that winter, too, he came within the orbit of Mrs. Stopford Green. She was Irish in the sense that Charlotte Shaw was, though she was to become much more deeply committed to Irish concerns. She was the daughter of the Archdeacon of Kells, and the widow of the historian, J. R. Green, and was already well known as a historian herself, and also as a philanthropist and also as a hostess. Her house on the river at Westminster was a rendezvous for the eminent. She was to play in Henry's life a part more interesting even than H. J. Elwes. At first she was merely an influential lady to be regarded from a respectful distance.

Among the great gardeners, one he found much to his liking was A. K. Bulley. On his way home from Ireland Henry stayed with the Bulleys in Cheshire. They had just the kind of house he liked. The living room was "a room, not a shop". It had "two great windows, no curtains, no bric-à-brac, a low ceiling, shelves of books at the windowless end; writing table in a corner, a few engravings of good pictures".[211] The dining-room was equally plain, and the servants' quarters, " 'drawing-room', kitchen, etc." were on as big a scale as the owners' (the Shaws' servants at Ayot St. Lawrence were by no means so comfortable). There was a roomy hall "where one can shake off rain and mud".[212]

The garden was still in the making. The ground round the house was being planted with shrubs. There was an experimental section for herbaceous plants, and a long covered walk with nearly a hundred kinds of roses trained on a pergola. The pergola seems to have been a novelty to Henry as he explains the term: "Stakes are driven in and other stakes laid across them."[213] The view was immense: "The Dee, the sea, pine woods inland, farms only in the near ground, no villas."[214]

Mr. Bulley was particularly interested in acclimatising plants from abroad, and Henry must have impressed on him the beauties of the Chinese flora, for not long after this he wrote to Professor Isaac Bayley Balfour of the Edinburgh botanic gardens to ask if he could recommend a man to collect for him. The result was the sending out of George Forrest, next after

Wilson in the line of great plant hunters in that field. In later years Mr. Bulley's daughter carried on the philanthropic tradition she had been brought up in by presenting the house and garden to Liverpool University, with an endowment, to be used for a botanic garden.

Both Mr. and Mrs. Bulley charmed Henry. "Mrs. Bulley gets about two frocks a year and hates to wear a hat and has long since given up gloves. I like my host and hostess very much. They are genuine."[215] The long account of his visit he wrote to Evelyn Gleeson ends, "I have to go a two-or-three day visit in October to see Elwes. It will be a contrast, I imagine."[216]

No doubt it was. What he can hardly have been prepared for at Colesbourne, Elwes's home, was the prevalence of stuffed animals. His host was not only a naturalist but also a very keen big-game hunter. A by-product of both these pursuits was his enthusiasm for taxidermy. He had done a bit himself, and considered it should rank higher as an art. "The lovely groups of birds in the South Kensington Museum are to my mind works of art of higher type than much of the painting and sculpture which one sees."[217] In his hall stood a she-bear killed in Norway, "beautifully stuffed for me by Herr Brunn, the well-known furrier at Trondhjem."[218] Also a boar. "As he was my first boar in Belgium and had a very good coat and tusks I had him stuffed in Brussels."[219] The extracts are from Elwes's *Memoirs*. Another account refers to stuffed wolves, elk and moose. Henry never mentions these big-game trophies. In China he had grieved to see wild animals destroyed. In Elwes's robust character there was no room for sentiment.

Mrs. Elwes was, as might be predicted, small, delicate and sensitive, and Henry seems at first to have felt more at home with her.

Elwes had served five years in the Scots Guards, and his battalion had once been marched to Chester to protect the arsenal from the Fenians, but the Fenians had cleared out before they arrived. His ideas of Ireland were derived from *The Experiences of an Irish R.M.*, which he pressed on his Irish guest. This book may be used as a way of testing the finer shades of nationality. Henry's reactions to it were tepid.

In April, 1902, a function was held in Henry's honour. The

Horticultural Club (not to be confused with the Royal Horticultural Society) gave a dinner for him and he was presented,
by the President of the R.H.S., with the Veitch Memorial
Medal. The head of the Veitch firm, who had sent out E. H.
Wilson, was in the chair. To quote the *Gardeners' Chronicle*: "A
capital programme of vocal and instrumental music served to
enhance the attractions of the evening, though, as it turned out,
the eloquence of the speeches generally, and particularly
the interesting nature of that of Dr. Henry, would have amply
repaid attendance."[220]

As Evelyn Gleeson was not able to be there we have Henry's
own account of this gratifying affair. He wore a frock coat,
with a gaudy tie which had just been sent him by his sister
Agnes, from America. "They had some great folks there and
letters of apology, telegrams were read, just as if I were a
personage. Sir W. T. Dyer proposed my health. He called me
his *dearest* friend, or words like that, and he was very charming
and blarneying."[221]

Henry's own speech, reported by the *Chronicle*, stressed the
opportunities for plant-collecting in China, and the advantage
of studying Chinese methods of horticulture which enabled
them, in favoured places, to raise as many as seven crops in one
season. He urged the Royal Horticultural Society to send out
an expedition with members better qualified than himself.
"He modestly argued that he had been the wrong man for the
task."[222] A real collector would not "as he did at the outset,
regard *Primula obconica* as simply a troublesome weed because
it was so abundant."[223]

While doing his best for China and horticulture, he did not
forget Ireland. He tells Evelyn Gleeson that he wound up by
reciting "The Lake Isle of Innisfree". They had none of them
heard it before.

13

During that winter of 1901–2 it gradually dawned on Henry that his vague idea of going in for forestry and his vague ambition of doing something for Ireland might be combined in a definite plan. The new Department of Agriculture surely ought to have a use for foresters. They might even create an opening for him if he qualified himself for the work.

Forestry was a subject that only a handful of people in the British Isles knew very much about. In France, Germany and Switzerland it had been practised on scientific lines since the seventeenth century. The Swedes had begun to take it seriously about fifty years back. The Americans and the Russians had for the past ten years been creating state forest reserves. The British had state forests in India—Henry knew a distinguished old German, Sir Dietrich Brandis, who had built up the Indian Forestry Service. In England and Scotland forestry was merely a pet topic of gentlemen with land, who were beginning to discover that trees, as well as beautifying a demesne, could be a paying proposition. Politicians, too, were inclined to regard tree-planting as the answer to all the problems of poverty-stricken rural areas. What nobody understood was that precepts derived from experience in France and Germany could not be applied wholesale under different conditions of climate and soil.

Forestry in Ireland had had a bad start, for this very reason. Some time in the eighteen-eighties, under Gladstone, a Danish "expert" had been sent over whose report was not really worth much. Then in the early years of the Conservative administration, when A. J. Balfour as Chief Secretary was "killing Home Rule by kindness", a public-spirited landowner presented a tract of land at Knockboy, in Connemara, for afforestation, and the government spent some thousands of pounds on planting it. They put in thirty or forty different kinds of trees, as nobody had any idea which were likely to grow. Henry told the

Departmental Committee on Forestry of 1908 they had acted on the principle of doctors who "gave you a prescription which had numerous drugs in it on the chance that you would get in one at least of them what you wanted".[224] (He had, of course, inside knowledge of medicine.) Almost all the trees at Knockboy failed. The land was exposed to all the winds that blew and nothing had been done in the way of providing shelter.

This historic waste of the taxpayers' money made the authorities cautious about doing anything more. Nevertheless, in 1895 or 1896, a better qualified expert was called in. This was Dr. Schlich, also German-trained. He had taken over from Sir Dietrich Brandis in India, and by 1902 was settled in England as head of the forestry school at Cooper's Hill. He saw possibilities in Ireland. A letter from him appeared in *The Times* suggesting that a pilot scheme might be begun in County Galway.[225] Plant a hundred thousand acres with birch, spruce and Scots pine; local farmers could work in the forest in winter, and pulp factories should be started to give employment to more people all the year round.

Henry obtained an introduction to Dr. Schlich, and in February had a talk with him. From him he got an inkling of the complexity of the subject, but he was confirmed in his opinion that it was worth while. Henry was never deterred from embarking on a course of study by the size of the field to be covered. Once again he "plunged in".

As he told Evelyn Gleeson, "I intend to try and get this forestry affair, though I feel rather incapable in some ways. If I don't get it I don't see what I can do practical and definite."[226]

What he hoped to get was, first the blessing of the Department of Agriculture on his entrance to the school at Nancy, which might not open its doors to an unaccredited outsider, and secondly some help in defraying his expenses, possibly a travelling scholarship. Also, perhaps, some idea of his prospect of future employment. With all this in mind he wrote to the Secretary, Mr. T. P. Gill. Mr. Gill advised him to formulate a detailed scheme and submit it in writing. This transition from the nebulous to the practical called for much thought and took up most of the spring. In May he went to Ireland again.

Evelyn Gleeson also wanted to do something for Ireland. She and Henry often talked of it, and he claimed afterwards to have given her the idea that developed into the Dun Emer Industries. He certainly helped her to act on it. Together they set out to launch a revival of craftsmanship in Ireland, on the lines laid down by William Morris.

They intended to found a craft centre on the model of Kelmscott Manor, where crafts could be taught, standards upheld, and fine work produced. Funds would come both from fees for training and from the sale of the craftwork. Partly it would be art for art's sake. but if the products of the centre became known and praised aboad, it would be a fine way to raise Irish national morale.

It was quite a practical proposition, for Evelyn Gleeson had just the contacts most likely to prove useful both at the artistic and the commercial end. Her friends the Yeats family had known Morris well (he had died five years earlier). Lily Yeats had learned embroidery from his daughter. Elizabeth Yeats was interested in typography and was in touch with Emery Walker, who was the inspiration behind the Kelmscott Press. Through members of Morris's group it would be possible to obtain instruction in the technique of almost any craft they wished to practise.

On the business side, Miss Gleeson could turn for help to her friends in the Irish Agricultural Organisation Society, George Russell and Susan Mitchell, both of them a remarkable blend of sense and sensibility, who could be trusted to sympathise.

Susan Mitchell was a Sligo girl, orphaned young, who had lived for a while with the Yeats. She had a satirical gift which expressed itself in light verse, and also ranked as a serious poet. She was assistant to George Russell, the Secretary to the Society, which existed to foster the co-operative movement.

George Russell or A. E. (a pseudonym he took from his pleasure in the word "Aeon") was the most singular genius ever to be employed in an organising capacity even by a voluntary body. He was a talented though undisciplined painter. As a poet he was overshadowed at that time only by Yeats. That same spring, his performance as a Druid in his own play *Deirdre* had been the highlight of a production which, though small scale, contained the germ of the new Irish Theatre. He sprang from a very humdrum if not humble, background, was shabby and neglected in his person, yet he impressed people with his authority even when he told them fairy tales. He was a visionary, given to metaphysical theorising derived mainly from Theosophy. Yet he could be thoroughly practical. For years he had held down the job of organising local banks for the co-operative movement. He travelled all over Ireland addressing meetings, and gained recruits by the sheer humanity of his approach.

In the hands of A. E. and Susan Mitchell, with H. J. Norman who then edited its journal *The Irish Homestead*, the Irish Agricultural Organisation Society took in more than banks, bacon factories and creameries. It was ready to nurture any tender sprout of home crafts or cottage industries and encourage any venture connected with the useful arts.

Henry threw himself heart and soul into plans for the centre—"the settlement" as they called it at first. Besides having great hopes of the scheme itself, he had a secondary reason for pressing it on his friend. He thought it would be for the good of her health to live somewhere other than in London. For despite the operations she had gone through she was still not well. Her illness was tubercular. She needed pure air. In Dublin one could live in real country not far from the city, and this, he felt, would be ideal for her.

He spoke of the plan to everyone whom he thought likely to be interested in helping Ireland, or in creative work. An obvious person to approach was Mrs. Stopford Green. He wrote to Evelyn, who did not know the lady: "Mrs. Green is very nice but you would get on with her much better than I would, as she would utilize me, whereas it is the exact contrary that is wanted."[227] Evidently he was a little nervous of such a managing person. Mrs. Green was sympathetic but very busy, and all she did at that stage was to put them in touch with a member of parliament from Ireland, a Mr. McCann.

The Yeats sisters came into the scheme. Their parents, conveniently, were moving to Dublin that spring. Elizabeth had consultations with Emery Walker and T. J. Cobden-Sanderson, who were then running the Doves Press together.

She took a month's course in printing at the Women's Printing Society in London and began looking round for a press. Evelyn Gleeson herself, already a trained designer, went into the technical side of carpet and tapestry making. Henry, while in Dublin, went with H. J. Norman of the I.A.O.S. to look at possible houses. In July Evelyn went over herself and decided on one that was to let near Dundrum. It was a pleasant, large, late-Georgian country house with a garden, about four miles south of the city centre, on rising ground where the fields began. The only thing wrong with it was its name, "Runnymede". Feeling that the associations of this were too purely English, she rechristened it "Dun Emer", the fort of Emer, after an Irish queen renowned for her skill in needlework.

Henry's own plans advanced less rapidly. The visit he made to Ireland in May that year did not get him much forrader with the Department, but it brought him new friends and showed him new sides of Irish life. This time he travelled all the way to Donegal, to stay with the Laws of Marble Hill.

They were people after his own heart, not fixed in a religious or social pigeon hole, but full of good will and doing all they could for those around them. They were Protestant country gentry, but Hugh Law had just been elected a Nationalist member for West Donegal, a seat he held till 1918. They were great friends of A.E., who for many years had his own cottage in their grounds and retreated there in his holidays. Henry may have met the Laws through A.E., or it may have been the other way round. They all came together in their zeal for the awakening of Ireland.

Always aware of his duty to his host, Henry read on the boat going over a speech by John Redmond, for which Hugh Law had supplied the data. Redmond was the leader of the Irish party, and how it had changed since the days of Parnell! Formerly it had made the most of its nuisance value; it was now sunken in respectability, and this sadly diminished its popular appeal. The speech was very dull. Henry wondered if the party couldn't be more up to date in its handling of public relations. In a note to Evelyn he said, "I am going to make several suggestions to Law with regard to diagrammatic and world-informing ways of presenting certain facts of Irish life."[228] He was alive to the possibilities of conveying statistics by symbols and diagrams, a method that has bridged language barriers and greatly simplified the dissemination of knowledge.

As usual he talked to fellow-passengers. On the boat he elicited from a couple of Lancashire business men—"coarse, strange creatures"[229]—that the employment of married women and young children was what kept down wages in the mills. In the train all across Ireland he chatted with a Presbyterian minister, an ex-Galway student, who was "lucid, direct and sympathetic".[230] He laid himself open to impressions and jotted them down for Evelyn. His letters are full of vignettes like an artist's sketchbook.

There was the great new Catholic cathedral at Letterkenny with two miserable cabins nearby; one had a pig's carcase hanging in the door. The innkeeper's daughter was practising *San Toy* on an inferior piano (*San Toy* was an operetta about China that had made a hit in London three years before). There was the arrival at the Laws'. His host had joined him for the last part of the journey, and after a long drive in the rain through desolate country they found a bonfire blazing and men came out with torches to welcome them. On Henry's first Sunday there was an unforgettable scene in the chapel: "A very poor building full of people, most of them anaemic and underfed, all pious and good. A coffin was before the altar, the body of a young man. Beside it, buried in a shawl, a young woman in intensity of grief—she never uttered a sound, but wretched beyond all expression lay prostrate in the shawl beside the coffin."[231] He did not enquire the details of the tragedy. Henry had an artist's eye for such scenes, their meaning for him was symbolic, generalised, an expression of the soul of things.

It is interesting that he had gone to Mass with the Laws' maids. In Ireland it was impossible not to be of some religion, and broadly speaking it was Protestantism for the gentry and Catholicism for the masses. But the religion of the Laws was not the "black" Protestantism Henry had hitherto encountered in Ulster, and which seemed to him "a mere spectre, a dry, formal thing without emotion or feeling".[232] He soon found that he and they had the same notion of Christianity. They loved their neighbours. They lived in close sympathy with the country people, knew the local fairy lore, and understood how it could blend with simple, rustic faith.

They knew, too, how much of the country people's earnings were spent in public houses. "The building of the great cathedral is defensible when one considers that £13,000,000 are spent on drink in Ireland every year."[233]

Marble Hill was beautifully situated between the mountains and the sea. Mrs. Law was more devoted to her garden than anything, but there was a great deal going on. The house was a centre of warmth and hospitality. A barn had been converted into a hall for the use of the local people. There was a dance there one night. Henry found the Irish reels quite different from those at the Gaelic League dances in the Athenaeum Hall. The highlight of his visit was a play, written and produced by the Laws' friend Miss Norah FitzPatrick, who was living with them at the time. Henry was greatly taken with Miss FitzPatrick. She was creative and energetic, a woman of the world with a warm heart. She had done social work in London. Her sister was Lion Phillimore, a great friend of the Shaws. He talked to her about "the settlement" and later on she joined forces with Evelyn Gleeson.

The time was not all spent in merrymaking. Henry's host took him to a meeting of Poor Law Guardians, to see for himself how the old Poor Law, absurdly out of date, rendered difficult the giving of relief. It was a subject on which Mr. Law felt strongly. Seven years later he was still crusading against the Poor Law, when he published a pamphlet on it, but the dead weight of this antiquated legislation took very much longer to lift.

Henry visited his brother Tom and his sister Matilda, and then went back to Dublin to try again, as he had already done on his way over, to get some answer from the Department of Agriculture. The Secretary, Mr. Gill, was in London, so he drew blank. There was no getting hold of Mr. Gill in London either. The next year's course at Nancy would begin in the autumn, so Henry was getting anxious.

In July he joined his sister Mary and her husband for a holiday in the French Alps, and took the opportunity to visit the School of Forestry and have an interview with the director. He was now quite determined to go there. All he asked from the

Department of Agriculture was the official credentials he needed in order to be admitted.

As Evelyn Gleeson had gone to Dublin to inspect Dun Emer, Henry asked her to try to see Mr. Gill. She apparently knew him personally, and in Ireland personal contact can work wonders.

"If possible eliminate from Gill any idea he may have that I am seeking any lucrative or easy billet. When I have got through Nancy I shall be worth a salary and will be able to get one anywhere, but I would, of course, prefer and only want really to work in Ireland. My course of action may seem unintelligible, yet it is plain enough."[234]

The situation was exasperating, but comic. Henry could easily have got the introductions he wanted in London where he knew everyone in the forestry world. His only idea in applying through the medium of the Department of Agriculture had been to pave the way for an Irish future. But in Ireland he was nobody. Either they forgot all about him, or his unusual disinterestedness made him suspect to the official mind. So his tale of frustration continues:

"Your account of your interview with Gill astonished me considerably. You tell me he said they were afraid that I would take it as a tacit promise of employment in Ireland if they were to get me into Nancy and *evidently they have taken no steps as yet*. . . . I understand perfectly (1) their objections to committing themselves, (2) their distrust of my capabilities, but I don't understand why they should not say yes or no and why they should *waste my time*. I dare say I can get into Nancy without them, but they will leave me too little time. . . . I don't think I could have a better advocate than you, but really, do you suppose for a moment that Gill believed you when you told him I didn't work for money and presumably had no money interest in the matter? His name is Thomas and I sent you a reference to the Gospel of St. John."[235] He adds a postscript: "You can mention to Gill incidentally that I have had a chat with Cadogan. A little snobbishness might help."[236]

Lord Cadogan was the Lord Lieutenant of Ireland who had sponsored the legislation which brought the Department of Agriculture into existence. He had that same month resigned his post, but his was still a good name to drop. Henry had met him at the opening of the Chelsea Botanic Gardens, an occasion which was the forerunner of the famous Chelsea Flower Shows. It was an event studded with gardening celebrities, among them Miss Ellen Willmott, and it was she who introduced Henry to the ex-viceroy. She was not a lady given to condescension. She was beautiful, intellectual, rich and proud, some would say spoiled. She could be capricious in her friendships. She was a personality with a temperamental kink, but Henry got on with her and always found her an ally.

Name-dropping produced no results. At the end of July he was getting frantic. "If Gill or the Agric. Board has not *yet* written concerning my getting into Nancy (at my own expense and with no promises expressed or implied) I must see if I can't go to the Foreign Office myself."[237] Then suddenly all was well. Perhaps the delay had been due to red tape in France, the reason was never really clear. At any rate, at the last minute, on August 21st, Henry received an official communication from Mr. Gill informing him that his admission to Nancy was approved by the French Minister for Agriculture.

His leave was up that September. He had then either to return to China or resign from the Customs Service. Some time during that anxious summer he took this decisive step.

Evelyn Gleeson came back to London, and was to stay there a few weeks longer than Henry, but now they were both busy with preparations for departure. He went with her to lawyers and helped her dispose of furniture. He was to be a shareholder in Dun Emer. He paid over his first contribution and ordered a saffron tie. Evelyn confessed she felt some regrets at leaving London. He had none. He was sure the air was unhealthy and the wood pavements gave people colds and the dust irritated their lungs. In pushing on the affair of the "settlement" he was sure he was doing the best thing for his friend.

Before he went to Nancy he had one more Irish interlude, and that a dazzling one. It was the week of the annual meeting of the British Association, and it took place in Belfast. Henry had a paper to read. It was on *The Lolos and Other Tribes of Western China*,[238] but the Lolos now were receding into the past and he had many other things to talk about. There was a full

programme of entertainment as well as instruction. He met
lots of Irish university people. He met Mr. and Mrs. T. P.
Gill and all was forgiven and forgotten. He found a very
general interest in the Gaelic revival, and best of all the Dun
Emer venture was already news. People began telling *him*
about it.

The Fishers put him up again, and he arrived at a better
understanding with Joe. Joe approved of his going in for
forestry, though he failed to grasp, any more than anyone else,
what an immense amount there was to learn. At least he no
longer regarded Henry as "heftless", and the Northern Whig
gave prominence to his paper. They parted on cordial terms.

Henry also managed to get over to Tyanee and lecture in the
local schoolhouse. There, he followed up his main discourse
with twenty minutes of exhortation to everyone to learn Irish.

After that, it was really farewell to Ireland, and a very much
longer farewell than he intended.

14

Henry's first letter[239] from France is signed Augustine instead
of Austin. Perhaps he was thinking of his name-saint making a
fresh start in middle life.

After a long, tiring night journey he looked out from the
train on wooded hilly country that reminded him of the
Hudson river valley. These wooded lower slopes of the Vosges
were far different from the evergreen rain-forests of south
Yunnan. The leaves were just taking on their autumn splen-
dour. It was clear, dry weather. In grassy clearings here and
there he saw parties picnicking.

Nancy was a fine town, well built and well laid out. The
streets were bright and clean. From the School of Forestry one
walked down an avenue of horse chestnuts to the public
gardens. Henry found lodgings looking out on these gardens.
Round the corner was the Place Stanislas with a good restaurant

where he could get meals *en pension*. Four small furnished rooms
with attendance cost him eighty francs a month. There was a
kitchen which he used as a bathroom and a hall where he could
keep his bicycle. Attendance included *café au lait* at 7.15 a.m.
and the dinner he took outside cost about two shillings, a third
of what he would have paid in London.

In Nancy he found all the provincial virtues flourishing and
worldly attractions not altogether absent. There were some
fine old churches and a picture gallery, and a theatre. "We
went to a play on Saturday night—a melodrama exactly of the
same type as one sees in London. It was absurd and foolish,
still they didn't make feminine charms a part of the attraction.
Indeed, the absence of barmaids and vulgar placards outside
the Casinos show that the French are a decent people. The
cocottes are few and well-behaved, taking their places in the
theatre with a certain dignity."[240] The women of Nancy
tended to be plain and dowdy; one seldom saw the Alsatian
national dress, which was much more becoming than the town-
made hats they wore. Yet he fancied it was they who kept
things going. "They are all active, thrifty, good managers
apparently, and they take care of the husbands."[241] The shop
assistants were charming. "The lady at the shoemaker's was so
tactful, clever, pleasant that it was quite a pleasure to order
one's shoes. Another lady measured my neck for a collar in a
most elegant way."[242] His landlady was motherly, far more
obliging than London ones. Farmers' wives in the country
were always ready to provide a snack of bread-and-cheese and
wine.

Some of the amenities were due to the presence of the
military. Nancy was a great army training centre. The quiet
was interrupted by bands and bugles and bursts of firing from
the ranges, for which large tracts of forest were reserved. Henry
had, up to then, been rather an admirer of martial virtues. Now
he had a revulsion of sentiment. There was so much too much
of soldiering. "When one sees the vast number of soldiers,
their foolish exercises, the work they do, useless except for
evil—one asks again what sort of civilization it is. Nanny
Griffin is right again by instinct."[243] She was the lady who
in London had lived "isolated among brachycephalic peace
people".[244] She belonged to the International League for

Arbitration. One of its members, M. Passy, came to speak in Nancy. He had a good attendance, and Henry thought made a good case.

The forestry students came from many countries and different social backgrounds, but they were all young, from twenty-two to twenty-four. They accepted Henry as a curiosity. His chief companion was a Russian prince, and he was conscious that they made an odd pair. Prince Lebedeff was handsome, polished, correct, well-dressed, a favourite with the fair. Yet he was "possessed with the idea that he ought to manage his own estate. I was rather astonished and enquired why he did not gamble and indulge in debauchery, horse-racing, automobilism, etc., but he has no taste for such noble occupations and has come here to work".[245] Henry despised snobbery, but he was sensitive to shades of breeding. He liked to think social superiority had a moral basis. He admired the prince's "frankness and want of cunning or reserve, which seem so characteristic of the ordinary scheming members of society, who are always talking with some aim of a material kind".[246] It is a mark of the well-bred to be above striving, as it is their luck not to have had to strive. He could not help being amused at the prince's own lofty disdain for class distinctions. Everyone who did not belong to his own order was "a simple peasant".

The weather at first was sunny with the pleasant tang of autumn, and there was the atmosphere of expectancy that hangs about an educational centre at the beginning of a new course. In November the mists began to gather. "Even the campanula bells in the forest had drooping heads, and plants with leaves that could sleep were all folded up and shut in against the damp fog."[247] Then came a sudden week of hard weather, the thermometer down to minus ten degrees Centigrade. The country looked beautiful under snow, but Henry's rooms were cold. "Wood as a combustible is nice in October, a delusion in December."[248] And most of the time there was no sun.

He settled down to work and found the going hard, so hard that he could not take time off. He had been given letters of introduction to local families but he did not present them. In spite of the contacts he had with French speakers in China he found the language a difficulty. The lectures required an extensive vocabulary. It also turned out to be necessary to learn some German. A German fellow student gave him an hour a day five days a week. The outdoor work also was strenuous. He was trying to master a complex subject through the medium of two foreign languages in a course designed for native speakers and for students half his age.

The field work was what interested him. Lectures, he decided, were mediaeval and ought to be abolished in favour of the Socratic method. But in the forests he learned what scientific cultivation could achieve. Tropical trees that grew to great heights were useless for timber. They were strangled by undergrowth and preyed on by parasitic plants. Here he saw oaks and beeches densely planted, clear of undergrowth, rank upon rank of tall trunks without branches, up to eighty feet high. Higher up were silver firs and spruce. "To give one example of the value of these forests, the 2,400 acres belonging to the hospitals of Nancy yield an annual income by the sale of timber of £4,000 net."[249]

There was no planting different kinds at random, as had been done at Knockboy. Altitude, moisture and soil were all considered. In Central Europe there is a natural succession of conifers as one climbs the mountains: silver fir on the lower slopes, spruce on the rocky soil where the snow drains down, larch highest of all. In the Vosges two or more species might be mixed, for reasons connected with the care of the soil and the seed. Young seedlings need soil nourished by humus, they need moisture and shade. In their early years they must be given protection overhead. Mature oaks and beeches will not bear crowding, but through their widely spaced trunks the wind blows, clearing away the leaves and drying up the soil. So to encourage seedlings the big trees are underplanted with low-growing coppice of trees like hornbeam, or mixed with shade-bearing trees like spruce. Cleaning and thinning, two separate stages, proceed as the seedlings grow. The coppice can be sold for firewood, hop poles, vine props and so on, but thinning is not done for the value of the stuff cut down, it is all for the sake of the timber trees. Felling, again, calls for experienced judgment, whether to cut whole sections, making great openings in the forest mass, or proceed selectively, taking two or three trees here and there. All this had been studied in

France over three centuries, since the time of Colbert, the great Minister of the great king, Louis XIV.

In Ireland, where there was less land under trees than in any other European country, such woods as remained were rapidly being cut down. Thanks to the recent land laws big estates were being broken up and sold to the former tenants, whose first act, naturally, was to clear them for farming. At the request of the Department of Agriculture, Henry composed a report[250] on yet another aspect of forestry: the laws which in France, Germany and Russia controlled the upkeep of woods in private hands, and imposed restrictions on felling. He did not think such regulations could be enforced in Ireland. There was such complete ignorance of forestry that they would only provoke resentment. He did think the Land Acts gave the Department a great opportunity to acquire land for forestry to be carried on by the state. He was thanked for his advice and his report was put on the files, where it stayed for another four years.

In the dead of winter the roads were too muddy for excursions, and the dull grind of theoretical work went on without respite. Cold, bored and homesick, Henry subsided into his recurrent depressive phase. Not the most flattering tributes could revive his spirits. Sir Joseph Hooker dedicated to him the December number of that famous publication, *Curtis's Botanical Magazine*. On the front page of Robinson's *The Garden* he found the phrase: "Men of the rare quality of Dr. Henry." He wrote to Evelyn Gleeson, "This appreciation should be consoling but it is not. If only I had some practical gifts, some enthusiasm, some divine fire!"[251]

"The fact is, to be a forester requires years and years, it is like anything else, it can't be learned in a few months, i.e., by me, and it is a terrible thing really for me to be always in exile, and in order to learn all that is required I shall want much time and money. I rather despair and wonder if I were wise to undertake what is really so serious an avocation. I want to use what brains I have, and I seem so stupid."[252]

The progress from amateur to professional is hard.

Evelyn Gleeson, too, sometimes wondered if she had been wise. Her first six months at Dun Emer brought their own worries. She was inexperienced in business, and unforeseen expenses made her nervous. Relations with her colleagues were not invariably harmonious. Her own health had not improved; the benefits of pure air tended to be offset by anxiety. Nevertheless, the craft centre was now in being.

Dun Emer was furnished and decorated. The drawing-room had moss green walls, the dining-room was papered in dull gold and furnished with carved oak. On the wide staircase leading to the first-floor workroom the walls were peacock blue. The Embroidery Room, large and sunny, was shared by the workers at tapestry and weaving. Elizabeth Yeats had installed her press. In the Printing Room A.E. had done a mural. Could Henry have meant this when he complained in one letter of "too much prevalence of weirdness"?[253] He liked A.E., but his taste in art was for the straightforward; he admired a jaunting car drawn by Jack Yeats.

Henry's views on art were not Philistine. He understood it could not be mere imitation. His attitude to flower painting, as distinct from botanical illustration, is worth recording. "I agree with Lolly (Elizabeth) Yeats about painting natural flowers. It is really inartistic. One cannot select. They are lovely things themselves, and the better the imitation the worse the effect. A glass or wax flower makes one ill. A landscape is very different, as there selection is possible and a painter can put some mind, something human into the picture."[254]

Miss Lily Yeats taught embroidery and a Miss Clarke gave lessons in tapestry weaving. Among the pupils was May Kerley, a niece of Henry's. The Laws' friend, Miss Fitz-Patrick, had taken up bookbinding and was in correspondence with Miss Gleeson about joining them.

Henry took the keenest interest in all these developments. He longed to be with his friends. He filled his letters with advice on everything from getting the drains inspected to the best method of keeping the books. The garden, he thought, might pay its way, whether or not it was considered to rank as an art. Why not propagate out-of-the-ordinary plants? He wrote to Thiselton-Dyer, to Miss Willmott and to A. K. Bulley for seeds and plants to stock it. He wrote to Mrs. Stopford Green, urging her to call at Dun Emer when she was in Ireland. She wrote back about a project of social development in the

Boyne valley. "If your friends get a good gardener they might perhaps extend *that* work there. I will send you some pamphlets."[255]

With the approach of spring and the resumption of field work Henry's own studies became less dreary. The small spring flowers appeared to cheer him, and provide more food for thought. Why should *Anemone hepatica* be found wild in woods all over Europe and in northern China, yet not in England? The answers to such questions about tiny plants sometimes led to discoveries about the conditions that favoured the growth of trees. Nothing could be studied in isolation. Botany developed into plant ecology; the influence on living things of their surroundings.

He was impressed by the uses of trees apart from their value as timber. In the Alps they had an important function in preventing avalanches and landslides. They not only gave shelter from the wind; their roots bound the soil, tapped underground springs, regulated the supply of water and prevented floods. Breathing moisture into the air, they softened the climate. Years later he published a book on the importance of tree-planting round reservoirs.

Trees could be persuaded to grow, with proper care, on exposed rocky slopes, or on the acid soil of bogs. The bogs interested him particularly, thinking of Ireland. He sent to his brother seeds of American larch and white cedar, to try out in a boggy place.

Prince Lebedeff also was interested in peat bogs, but forestry in the high Alps is more concerned with road building, tunnelling and drainage. Much of the course was devoted to engineering, which for Henry was a waste of time. In the Easter vacation he and his Russian friend got hold of an outside forestry expert and went with him to study plantations on peat. The year's work would end in June with some long excursions, to which Henry was looking forward, but he was more and more impatient with the theoretical work at the college, and began to doubt if it would be worth staying another year.

Unfortunately there was no sign of a job in Ireland. About this time another old college friend applied for a post under the Department of Agriculture, and Evelyn Gleeson put in a word for him with Mr. Gill. A propos of this Henry wrote: "I don't want you to log-roll for me the least little bit. I will tell you how it is. I don't expect ever to have anything to do with the Department officially. I shall probably now go on to the end studying forestry and its allied subject botany, and if I am any good after some years they may come to me. I shall be courted and won't do any courting."[256] It was typical of his pride, and it proved prophetic.

He had enough to live on, modestly, between his pension and his savings. His tastes were simple and he had no dependants. Some of his friends wondered why he did not go back to China, where he could have lived in affluence, but he would have had to be poor indeed to return to that land of despair. The great thing was that he had now found an absorbing vocation. Only how was he to pursue it? The training he had embarked on so hopefully was not helping him to the knowledge he wanted.

Elwes's proposition for *The Trees* came at exactly the right psychological moment.

Elwes, ever since he had inherited his father's estate some ten years earlier, had been feeling the need for a work of reference that would help a landowner to decide what trees to plant. There were the eight volumes of Loudon's *Arboretum et Fruticetum*, of 1838, but he found these out of date and also often inaccurate. He suspected they were based on other books rather than experience. Apart from this there had been nothing of the same scope since Evelyn's *Sylva* of 1664. Professor Sargent of Harvard had just brought to completion a *Sylva* of North America in fourteen volumes. Elwes's project was to do the same thing for the British Isles.

It was a tremendous task, but Elwes was a person of tremendous energy. He seems to have been prepared to shoulder most of the work himself. When he wrote his monograph on *The Genus Lilium* twenty years before, he had engaged a professional botanist, J. G. Baker, to do the scientific descriptions, which was simply a mechanical task. This may have been all he had in mind when he first approached Henry about *The Trees*, though he found in him a very active collaborator. All published references to the authors, in or on *The Trees*, imply that they worked as partners on level terms. In fact Elwes took all the financial risk and paid Henry a salary, thus enabling him to undertake the task. The book was not aimed at making a profit. To Elwes it was simply a useful job that cried out to be done.

To Henry it was a unique opportunity to acquire the knowledge of trees that he so greatly desired. This is clear from two letters he wrote in April, 1903, to Thiselton-Dyer. He consulted this good friend in confidence as to whether he could depend on Elwes to stick to his intentions. "It is a serious step getting in tow with anyone financially."[257] He also asked Thiselton-Dyer's opinion on his own ability to do the work. Sir William's reply was satisfactory on both points, but he wondered if Henry was wise to abandon his forestry course, which had another year to run. Henry pointed out that Elwes's plan offered more chance of practical experience. "It would mean going about, seeing forests in Europe and possibly in America, and it would be a great *education* for me."[258] "I now know enough theory to observe with intelligence and report with accuracy."[259] "And, of course, connexion with the publication of an interesting book would be a good thing for me."[260]

He did not rush into the project without careful consideration, but he was certainly excited about it. In letters to Evelyn Gleeson he refers to Elwes mysteriously as "Dives". The only other time that in his letters he bestows a nickname on anyone is when he confides in his old friend concerning a lady "Perdita" with whom his emotions were deeply involved.

In May he went to London, saw Elwes and stayed with him at Colesbourne, and committed himself to the collaboration. He packed a great deal into that visit, saw a "superb" flower show at the Temple, was guest of honour at a dinner of the Kew Guild, and had a chat with Miss Norah FitzPatrick about adding bookbinding to the crafts of Dun Emer. Between some of these engagements he fitted in a flying visit to Dun Emer itself.

He was delighted with all he found there. The pupils made him think of his own wild plants from China; how they responded to cultivation, "which always remind me that I have done something—that I have made the world richer and more beautiful, so do you, so will you more and more."[261]

Indeed by 1903 Dun Emer was a shining facet of the Irish cultural renaissance. The aim of the press was to produce the new literature of Ireland in worthy editions. It brought out new books, not beautiful reprints. The first came out that July, *In the Seven Woods* by W. B. Yeats. (It had nothing to do with forestry.) In August they had in the garden another performance of A.E.'s *Deirdre*, and Yeats's *Cathleen ni Houlihan*.

Henry wished he could be with them in body as he was in spirit. Writing to thank Evelyn Gleeson for her hospitality he said, "One of my reasons for thinking of Elwes's scheme is that I see in it good possibilities of propaganda. I will be *your* best advertiser."[262] He would be moving round among people with money to spare, and he would sell them the new Ireland.

The excursions that wound up the forestry year were physically the toughest part of the course, but Henry revelled in them. They went to the high Vosges, the Rhone valley, the Jura, the Pyrenees and the Landes. "We cover immense distances and I have scarcely slept more than five hours any night, and there are the dinners which end late and the early starts in the morning. All this sounds like an apology for not writing, but I don't feel guilty. In fact I feel quite happy and gay."[263]

He also made a private excursion to Switzerland, to meet a famous botanist at Basle, and to visit poor Susan Mitchell in a sanatorium. He had been anxious about her, and had written to her colleague in the I.A.O.S., H. J. Norman, urging that she should go away for rest and treatment[264] and, whether or not it was due to his intervention, she did so. He found her "like an Andromeda, chained to a barren rock. Parts of the country are really hideous. The English tourist accepts it all as beautiful, and for him and his like there are wearisome hotels, where the people discuss inane subjects."[265] The Swiss-German hoteliers were "vulgar" (one of Henry's severest epithets) and the Alps looked small to one accustomed to the vastness of China: "So narrow you can cross them in two days!"[266] But a distant view of the Jungfrau from Mont d'Or in the Jura "made my heart stop beating".[267]

Susan Mitchell's plight had reminded him of Caroline. "Life has made me so sympathetic with certain kinds of sick people."[268] Happily in her case the treatment had good results. Henry also passed through Lourdes, "very striking, the wonderful devotion and faith there *is the miracle*".[269]

Lourdes was on his way with the foresters to the Landes, and this was the climax of their excursions. He had been enchanted with the Pyrenees, and the Basque people in their isolation reminded him of the Lolos, and at Fuenterabbia over the frontier he fell in love with the Spaniards, "dignified, content, proud, pious, in total disagreement with the modern world".[270] But the Landes was a victory for the nineteenth century, a miracle of devotion and faith on an earthly plane. Where eighty years earlier there had been a million and a half acres of malarious waste land—sand dunes, marshes and lagoons— there now stretched a vast pine forest full of villages and industries.

In a lecture to the Royal Dublin Society the following year, Henry described how the waste land had been reclaimed "by enlisting the ordinary forces of nature, the wind and plant-growth".[271] Palings and wattle fencing hold up the sand as it drifts in from the sea. The banks thus raised are planted with marram grass, gradually the dunes are stabilised and form a sheltering mound. Behind it the land is sown with mixed seed of furze and broom and maritime pine. The work has often to be renewed, but a desert has been made healthy and productive. The trees supply timber and resin for turpentine. In the south cork oaks are mixed with the pine, and their bark yields corks for the wine trade of Bordeaux.

After these forestry excursions Henry could not doubt that this science was worth the devotion of half a lifetime. He only wished he had made an earlier start.

15

Henry had always maintained that a hereditary wealthy class like the British nobility and gentry justified its existence by being a breeding ground of individualists. Out of its ranks came inspired amateurs who found the world their oyster, who opened it by travel, who gave new directions to art and science and took on tasks that poorer men or public bodies could never contemplate.

Such, undoubtedly, was H. J. Elwes. An intrepid traveller and distinguished naturalist, he was also nobly generous. Among other benefactions he subscribed a thousand pounds towards the Royal Horticultural Society's hall in Vincent Square, and he enabled the R.H.S. to buy up the *Botanical Magazine* and save it from bankruptcy. He shouldered all the responsibilities of a landowner, sat on board and bench and ran his estate in a businesslike way, but on coming into it he had not dropped other enthusiasms. Mrs. Elwes might be told any morning, "My dear, I am off to-morrow to South America." In 1900 he had gone to Bosnia to look at spruce forests, and the winter when Henry was at Nancy had been spent by him in Chile studying monkey-puzzles and southern beeches.

A charming sketch of him was contributed some years ago to the *Cheltenham Chronicle*[272] by Colonel R. B. Molesworth, whose father was his estate agent. In the eyes of a small boy he was a fabulous figure, a giant with a blue-black beard and a thumb stick six feet high (it had a metal spud for rooting up weeds). Children were on their best behaviour in his presence, but not overawed; he treated them as real people and taught them good manners by example.

The Trees of Great Britain and Ireland, planned in five volumes and expanding to seven, was a heroic conception. The need was for information not only about trees that grew naturally in Britain, but on trees from anywhere in the world that *would* grow in Britain. The first intention was to deal only with timber, not ornamental trees, but it proved impossible to draw a rigid line. Not satisfied with hearsay, Elwes and Henry set out to inspect between them good specimens of every kind of tree growing in the British Isles and to study them under the headings: varieties, distribution, cultivation and propagation, and economic uses. In the case of non-native trees, they ascertained by research the date of their original introduction, and if such trees seemed likely to be of value they were prepared to go and investigate the conditions that suited them in their native habitats. As will be seen, this involved them both in some stupendous journeys. In some cases they found that the finest existing specimens of exotic trees were those growing in the British Isles, and, as a French reviewer pointed out, this gave their book a value abroad as well as at home.[273]

The seven volumes are a fascinating "Who's Who" of trees of that period, many of which still survive. They are also a compendium of most useful information that does not date. Yet they are unknown to the reading public, and even the present generation of foresters for the most part have only heard of them. *The Trees* is hard to come by, even in libraries. Only five hundred copies were ever published, and most of these were taken by subscribers at fifteen guineas the set.

This was due to Elwes's aristocratic approach to the business of publication and distribution. His lofty attitude is calculated to make humbler authors gasp. He decided to be his own publisher, since no commercial firm could have given him the co-operation he required. "No one can really tell when he begins a work of this magnitude what it will grow to, what it will cost, or how long it will take. If it is all written out ready for publication, the loss of knowledge will be immense, because one learns as one goes and fresh sources of knowledge are constantly being opened up."[274] So the type was kept standing indefinitely. Both the authors found it easier to revise in proof than manuscript. Henry read the proofs of the first volume twelve times. Each of them perpetually added footnotes. The wonder is that the work ever got into print.

Elwes also disdained to spend anything on advertising, or even to distribute copies to the Press. But as in the course of collecting information he and Henry had contacted almost every arboriculturist in the British Isles, the book hardly needed any further promotion. The limited edition was almost immediately out of print. The expenses of publication were covered, and the subscribers had a good investment, for within a few years a set was sold for £75. The pity was that *The Trees* was always beyond the reach of the ordinary general reader.

If Elwes planned, financed and organised the undertaking, it was Henry's part in *The Trees* that made of it, besides a reference book on arboriculture, a permanent contribution to tree botany. He found the nomenclature of trees in a muddle. As well as doing all the botanical descriptions, he took pains to list all the names by which each tree was scientifically known and to select, or if necessary supply, the correct name according to the rules of international botany. The practice at Kew had always been to use the name first given to a plant when it was classified under its genus. But after he had begun the work on this basis there came in the Vienna rule, which has led to unceasing complaints from ordinary gardeners. This rule is that the first name ever given to the species must apply, even if it has been re-classified under a different genus, and so we have *Pyrus japonica* turning into *Cydonia lagenaria*, and perpetual changes rung on names which are difficult enough already. The Vienna rule necessitates immense research, and makes it difficult ever to be sure that a name is finally correct. In a good many cases where the oldest specific name should have been used, Henry preferred the name by which foresters would more easily recognize the trees intended. His naming of trees was not definitive, but it eased the path for botanists coming after him.

He also devised ingenious keys to the identification of trees, for a forester must be able to recognise them as young saplings, even before they have flowered or borne fruit. For absolute accuracy a botanist must have fruit and flower, but for working use Henry's way of classifying species, by leaves and twigs and the position of buds, has the advantage of being applicable at any stage of growth and any time of year.

He and Elwes shared between them the general work of hunting up fine trees and investigating their life histories.

They criticised each other's contributions but kept them separate, and each signed his items with his initials.

There was from the first a keen interest in the project in botanical circles. Henry was given a room at Kew to work in, and to use as an address on the elegantly headed notepaper with which he was soon provided. Everyone was friendly and helpful. The job carried some prestige. He had hardly settled down to it when he had a flattering offer of quite another kind.

Mention has been made of his *Notes on the Economic Botany of China*,[275] the booklet published in an edition of a hundred at Shanghai. The American government had recently recognised its usefulness and re-issued it, as in those days it was entitled to do, without remunerating the author. It had made a reputation for Henry in the States, and the government now was prepared to sponsor an expedition to central China, if Henry would conduct it. He was approached by a high official and invited to name his own salary. But all the reasons he had given for refusing a similar suggestion from Sargent were more than ever valid. All the information he could give was at the U.S. government's disposal, but even if he had not already signed a contract with Elwes, he could not have been tempted to return.

He ruefully told Evelyn Gleeson, "It is hard to find oneself so much cajoled by strangers and that there is no foothold in Ireland."[276]

It was some consolation that the business of *The Trees* would take him often to Ireland. He egged on all his friends to make enquiries, Evelyn's relations at Athlone, H. J. Norman through the I.A.O.S., and the influential and widely connected Mrs. Stopford Green.

The Trees soon became "the millstone to which my neck is tethered".[277] Henry was in a familiar dilemma. He had to have work to do; he was restless without an object in life. Once committed to a task he gave himself up to it; he never did anything by halves. Yet he was never completely single-minded. His active intellect ranged over many fields, and his accumulated knowledge of many subjects haunted him with a sense of work undone. The Lolos had to be abandoned, and the learning of Irish. He still went occasionally to meetings of the Irish Literary Society, but all that winter he had little time for private life.

The work itself brought with it social contacts of an exalted kind. A social climber could not have had a better springboard. The authors' list of acknowledgments, starting with the king, includes six dukes, four marquesses, eighteen earls and numerous minor titles. Henry went to many great houses, and though his business could have been done with the steward, the owner usually took a personal interest. "I had a letter to the gardener. The earl, however, sent a car to meet me, gave me lunch, and was very nice indeed. The Countess was delightful too. Countesses apparently are beauties, which is more than he can said for mere Baronesses."[278] "This letter reads like a court journal, but that is the amusing part of it, as I have no more snobbery than a cat."[279]

In the spring he lectured at Manchester, Limerick and Belfast. Father Finlay, who was allied with Sir Horace Plunkett in the co-operative movement, asked him for a series of articles, but his contract with Elwes bound him not to publish anything on trees except in connection with the book.

In the summer he joined again in part of the French foresters' excursions, then did an equally arduous tour in Scotland with the English Arboricultural Society. "We have been getting up at five and catching trains at all hours, sandwiches in pocket. Occasionally we had sumptuous lunches but they waste time."[280] There was much to be learnt in Scotland, where there had long been a lively interest in forestry. He saw there how successfully trees could be grown on unreclaimed peat.

He came home from these journeys to piles of letters. Requests for information brought counter-requests for advice on planting. The correspondence snowballed.

The worst of so much social life was the need to keep presentable. Henry grudged the time as much as the money. He made a happy discovery—the dry cleaners. "I have solved the dress question. By sending my old clothes to Pullar's they come back new. It is a wonderful invention. Only one luxury— *shoes* superfine I shall have and good."[281] Another new discovery was Lyons' Popular Café. Dining there was both cheap and fun—"Hundreds of people crowding in like into a theatre and band playing—food profuse, not cooked individually, wine cheap and good."[282]

He spent the fees for some lectures on his share as one of the hosts at a dinner for his old friend Thiselton-Dyer, who had been knighted, reached a pinnacle of eminence as botanical adviser to the Secretary of State for the Colonies, and was now on the brink of retirement. This meant changes on the staff at Kew. Henry's friends canvassed his chances of an appointment there, but he himself did not rate them high and declined to exert himself in that direction.

He also came out of his shell, reluctantly, for a dinner of the Linnean Society. This grave body had been persuaded by Elwes to admit women as Fellows, and notably Miss Willmott. Ellen Willmott ranked with Gertrude Jekyll and William Robinson as one of the great gardeners of the day, and she practised on them the art of one-upmanship, as her fortune enabled her to do. They laid out great gardens in England and published books on them; her garden at Warley Place was already famous, and she was planning one of fifty acres on the Riviera. She was compiling, not a popular book, but the ultimate work of scholarship on *The Genus Rosa*. To be among the first women Fellows of the Linnean Society set the seal on her renown. Henry, with his well-known sympathy for feminine emancipation, was an obvious choice for a speaker. "It was thought I would be a proper person to enliven the proceedings, they are usually dry."[283] Sad to say, the evening was wrecked by a bore. Another Fellow, who had been allotted fifteen minutes for a chat on crustacea, spoke first and went on for fifty. Henry had to restrain his own eloquence, but he succeeded in pleasing Miss Willmott and she invited him to Warley.

Such visits multiplied. It was a great age of country life, every house had its traditions and treasures. He went to Arley Court, an old castle on the Severn with a Norman church and a manorial ferry; to Sir Walter Phillimore's, where they had a manuscript poem of Gladstone's; to H. Clinton Baker's who had all the original portraits of the Kit-Cat Club; to the Taylors of Sherfield Manor, who took him for drives in their numerous motor-cars (they were South African millionaires). Miss Willmott had a fine collection of musical instruments. He found she was a skilled photographer and also carved on

ivory. She outdid him in early rising and was up at five. In
the autumn of 1905 he went, like Society, to Scotland. "The
king was staying at the next house, and if I had remained
another day I should have met him as he visited Mr. Birk-
beck's garden and praised the eucalyptus trees. He had tons of
baggage and rather obstructed the route; monopolised all the
conveyances—I escaped by mail car."[284] At Sir Herbert
Maxwell's home, Monreith, he met one of the Bensons and
Andrew Lang, "the authors are queer, vain folk".[285] He went
on to join Sir John Sterling Maxwell's house party at Corrour,
where he met a titled Ulster lady who had never heard of the
Gaelic League. He spent three days in Edinburgh with Professor (later Sir Isaac) Bayley Balfour, a great promoter of
Chinese plant hunting. He then spent a night with Sir Archibald Hepburn, a descendant of Bothwell, whose house contained relics of Mary Queen of Scots. A meeting with Vicary
Gibbs, editor of *Cokayne's Complete Peerage*, resulted in an
invitation to his father's, Lord Aldenham's, where there was a
collection of fine old missals. Vicary Gibbs made the gardens
at Aldenham famous, and used to share their bounty by selling
surplus plants.

"Yesterday we went to Tring and crossed the Chiltern Hills
to Wendover, going through three parks belonging to the
Rothschilds. We called on the Hon. Charles and lunched on
gold plates with gorgeous footmen arrayed in sateen nethers,
gold breastplates with platinum buttons and iridium collars
and diamond and ruby turbans. The napkins of the finest
lawn were fringed with Bank of England five-pound notes,
and we drank nectar out of malachite goblets. We then rode
on zebras and chased emus through the park.

"All this would have happened but alas! Hon. Charles was
not at home."[286]

The very rich were not, to Henry, quite real people.

"As soon as the book is finished, I shall cut my aristocratic
connections and get away to Ireland, as it is no good going on
with mere pleasantness of life. However, of course, I exclude
Mrs. Green from this excommunication of the future, as I
hope she will remain my friend."[287]

L

16

During the summer of 1905 Henry had got to know Mrs. Stopford Green better, for she had carried him to Ireland in her train. She took him to stay with Lord Monteagle, who had fine trees, and she arranged for them both to be taken on a week's tour by a member of the Congested Districts Board. "Congested" districts were the loneliest and barest, the word was official jargon for places where the population, though sparse, was more than the land could support. Henry could there study the problem of land reclamation.

But more than this, Mrs. Green proved her worth when Henry at last brought her to Dun Emer. They found Evelyn Gleeson again in bad health. Among Mrs. Green's useful connections was her brother-in-law, Sir Lauder Brunton, a leading London physician. She knew much about doctors. She recommended a Dr. Wright. He happened to be on holiday in Ireland, and it was arranged for him to see Miss Gleeson on the way back.

Dr. Wright, who the following year became Sir Almroth Wright, was known for his work on microbic infections. He had introduced anti-typhoid inoculation and had developed therapeutic immunisation by vaccines, not for prevention but for treatment. He was among the great doctors of the period. Evelyn Gleeson consulted him again in London in the autumn and following spring, and followed his treatment with good results. In the latter part of her life she had much better health than ever in her youth.

This was just like Alice Stopford Green. She was an outstanding person, a blend of the Du Maurier lady and the Shavian intelligent woman, and by now she had really taken Ireland in hand. Historical research had convinced her that the Home Rulers had a case. She was working on a book, *The Making of Ireland and its Undoing*, which brought history to the nationalists' support.

Through being in the public eye as a philanthropist she had

recently met Roger Casement. He had written to her the year before asking for a subscription to his Congo Reform Association. As a British consul in the Belgian Congo he had exposed atrocities in a report that roused public opinion. He was Irish too, and, if he had not till then thought much about Irish politics, his sympathies were soon awakened. With his fine record and handsome person he would have been an asset to any hostess or any cause.

Henry and Evelyn Gleeson met Casement at Mrs. Green's in the autumn, while Evelyn was in London for treatment. They both admired him. But Mrs. Green's particular charm for Henry had less to do with Ireland than with her niece, Alice Brunton, with whom, in the following year, he discovered himself to be in love.

He had not meant to marry again. He would not marry for money, and his means were too small to support a wife with none. He was used, by now, to the single life. He had his long-standing friendship with Evelyn Gleeson. He sometimes discussed love and friendship with her. They understood each other from of old. With other women—he was depressed at the numbers of marriageable spinsters he encountered—he was careful not to give rise to romantic expectations. Though he complained to Evelyn, "It is exasperating that a man and a woman can't talk without there being some suspicion of romance,"[288] he respected the conventions. "It would be wrong for me to indulge in perilous friendships, as I am so little liable to fall into danger."[289]

"Friendship between men and women is very difficult, because love is so near, especially with women, and I think that spoils friendship. Of course love is most perfect, most beautiful, and it comes unexpectedly from heaven, and one cannot refuse it. Yet friendship is perfect also."[290]

Unexpectedly from heaven it came. His letters of the next two years unfold an idyll as unlikely as it is satisfactory.

Alice Brunton, always called "Elsie" to distinguish her from her aunt, Alice Stopford Green, was the eldest of the four children, two boys and two girls, of Sir Lauder Brunton, one of the leading physicians of the day. Her birth had been smiled on by no less a person than Henry's hero, Charles Darwin. On his advice her mother kept a journal of her development, which

was that of a healthy, normal baby. Later, Darwin remarked
of her, "How a child does cheerfullise a house!"²⁹¹ Cheerfulness characterised her. She had exactly Henry's idea of
"innocent gaiety". All the Bruntons had the knack of anecdote
and light verse and apt repartee. They were light hearted
though not light minded. The children had before them the
example of their father's dedicated hard work, without being
too much oppressed by it. "Father never minded how many
balls we went to or how late we came home provided we were
down to breakfast at eight o'clock next morning."²⁹²

Elsie, the eldest, had responsibility thrust on her rather early.
Her mother was not strong and often had to delegate duties to
her. They lived in a beautiful old house, 10 Stratford Place,
which took ten servants to run, and they entertained as was
expected of people in their position in those days. Elsie, taking
her mother's place, met her father's distinguished colleagues.
Perhaps she found younger men dull.

She was not considered pretty, but she might be now; she
can never have been plain. She was petite and agile and liked
clothes. She had learned ju-jitsu and reached the grade of a
black belt. She had an opportunity to go to America to
demonstrate the art, but her family did not care for the idea.

Elsie had an earnest side. With some of her school friends
she formed a society called "The Seekers", but what they
sought was a secret. Her mind, like Henry's, rejected dogma,
and though she belonged to the Church of England, she lived
in a climate of ideas derived partly from Theosophy and partly
from Hegelian notions of the Absolute and the Oversoul. These
systems of thought fitted in with each other and consoled people
for the loss of orthodox faith. Elsie, however, had not much
chance to be soulful, as she always had plenty of practical
matters on hand.

About this time she acted as hon. secretary for the entertainment committee of an International Congress for School
Hygiene, which met in London with her father as president.
There were six hundred delegates for whom some entertainment had to be provided every day. It was a great success.
Elsie received an order from the French government, with a
little pink button to wear. The congress resulted in a law
making physical examination compulsory in schools. Sir

Lauder Brunton was obsessed with the necessity of improving
national physique. Even as early as 1905 he thought the nation
might have to face a large-scale war.

One of the entertainments at the congress was an evening
garden party at Kew, with strawberries sent from Scotland
because the English crop was over, and Chinese lanterns in the
trees. It would be appropriate if this was where Henry and
Elsie Brunton met, but there is no record of it, and the Hon.
Secretary was probably too busy for dalliance.

They did meet, after they were already to some extent
acquainted, at a party given by the Cobden-Sandersons. T. J.
Cobden-Sanderson was a great typographer, a sort of godfather,
as we have seen, to the Dun Emer Press. They were political
left-wingers. Mrs. Cobden-Sanderson indeed was jailed some
months later as a militant suffragette. They were friends of
Keir Hardie, ex-miner and father of the Labour Party, who was
considered by many old-fashioned people a bit of a firebrand.
Henry had come across Keir Hardie in Scotland, and had taken
to him personally, though with reservations about his policies.
The Labour Party was making afforestation a plank in its
platform, and the Cobden-Sandersons had arranged for Henry
to lecture on it in the Morris Hall. So here he was at their
party, with Keir Hardie himself, John Burns of the L.C.C.,
Tom Kettle (an Irish M.P.), and a number of other serious-
minded middle-aged people. But the occasion transcended
politics: it was the Oxford and Cambridge Boat Race.

Henry had last seen the Boat Race just before he first went
out to China, in company with Evelyn Gleeson and a Miss
Harriet Weir who had left some tender memories. The air of
spring was perfumed with old romance. He had a long talk with
Miss Brunton, who had come with her aunt and perhaps was
a little stranded. The following Sunday he called for her in
the morning and took her to Kew, where among the flowers,
they continued their conversation on philosophic doubt. He
came home to lunch with her and her mother. A day or two
later Elsie and her aunt left for a holiday in Italy.

Henry was very busy. The season for country-house visiting
resumed with spring. He ran over to Ireland but stayed, this
time, with the Moores at the Botanic Gardens at Glasnevin,
in the pretty little Regency house allotted to the director.

Professor Sargent passed through London in April, and Henry spent several hours with him and Miss Willmott at Kew. The first volume of *The Trees* was now going through the press. At Colesbourne he and Elwes worked on the final proofs from 6.30 a.m. till midnight.

He received another honour. The Royal Horticultural Society conferred on him its Victoria medal, limited to sixty-three holders. On a visit to Wisley he noted with pleasure a large bed devoted to one of his favourites among his own finds, *Rehmannia angulata*. He had these things to comfort him when he felt depressed and overtired, and he did so, often. It might, he told Evelyn Gleeson, be a hang-over from malaria.

On the day when Mrs. Green and Miss Brunton returned from Italy Henry left for a three-day visit to Cambridge, to stay with a Fellow of King's, and lecture on Chinese Botany. Soon after he came back Mrs. Green asked him to dinner. Elsie Brunton was there "with rosy cheeks from Italian skies",[293] and Henry took her in. Roger Casement sat at the head of the table. Another guest was Hugh Law.

It is from then on that Henry refers to Elsie in letters as "Perdita". It had dawned on him that he was in love, and he did not think he had a chance. That summer he visited the Forest of Arden, but it was solely in the way of business. Disenchantment is his refrain. "The people whom I see and know give me everything I don't want."[294]

He did a lot of work and a lot of rushing about. Elwes said afterwards that he had worn out two motor-cars on *The Trees*. Henry never drove a car himself, but he was a veteran passenger by now. He had a beautiful Irish tweed made into "a semi-motor overcoat with large leather buttons". He toured French forests that summer with Lord Kesteven, a friend whose name appears in one of his earliest Chinese notebooks, evidently another adventurous travelling "milor". Among his lifelong forestry friends in France were M. de Vilmorin of the famous nursery dynasty and M. Hickel of Versailles. Henry came back from France very tired and found London very hot, but settled down to a programme of all work and no play. Then the work unexpectedly set him off again. At the end of July he sailed for the United States.

This was one of Henry's epic journeys. It had a great influence on his thinking on forestry, for it enabled him to study certain fast-growing conifers in their native conditions.

The expedition was sponsored by Lord Kesteven and Sir John Stirling Maxwell. Its main object was to obtain seed of *Larix occidentalis*, the western larch. Larch was the pet tree of early foresters. The European variety had been planted all over the British Isles. In the last few years it had been attacked by a disease, and valuable plantations had been destroyed. The western larch was believed to be immune from the disease, and was also a finer tree. Elwes had already tried twice to import seed, but had only secured a small supply. It did not set every year. Henry hoped to bring home enough to enable western larch to be tried out experimentally on a large scale in different places. He had an open mind about it himself, and was on the look-out for alternatives.

He was sure now that it was a mistake to base English forestry entirely on the experience of eastern France and northern Germany and Denmark. There, the summers were hot and dry and the winters hard. European larch grew very well in the milder, moister western islands, but the difference in climatic conditions accounted for its succumbing so readily to infection. West Scotland, Wales, Devon and Cornwall and Ireland, should grow the trees of the western part of north America, a region with some of the greatest forests of the world.

He went to Montana, Idaho, Oregon, and Washington state, from there into Canada as far as Vancouver, across the continent to Winnipeg, and back by way of Minnesota into the United States. It was comparable to the expeditions he had made in Hupeh and Sze-chwan. It was not the Wild West of the films, but forest country without trails or horses. In China he had been twenty years younger and had coolies to carry the luggage. Here, he wrote to Colonel Prain, the new Director of Kew, "One had to plunge into jungle and fallen timber and fight one's way laden with 40–50 lb. of a pack (food and a blanket). Food is flour, which we make into pancakes, bacon and coffee. Our party killed the white mountain goat and black bear."[295]

In Oregon he did go by horse stage, fifteen hours at a stretch. "Seventy miles by stage to Crescent City on the coast . . . an awful journey and it is threatening rain, but I can't think of turning back without seeing the redwood forest."[296] There was a worse form of transport in Montana: the Great Northern Railway. "I dread going on this," he told Prain. "Forty-five men killed in the last thirty days."[297] He spent some days with a railway gang and was shocked at what they told him of their working conditions, the long hours and accidents due to the badly laid track. He was also the guest of a goldminer. He talked with forest rangers and trappers. He saw gigantic redwoods, Oregon Douglas fir and Sitka spruce, in the forests of the mild Pacific coast, but found the larch growing best in the mountains, where the winter was hard and the summer dry.

He did not get as much seed as he had hoped, and not of the best quality. Larch has the peculiarity of ripening its cones very rapidly; they open and shed all in a week, and the good seed, being heaviest, falls out first. This was only beginning to be understood. As a result of Henry's enquiries a good supply of seed was sent over two years later and was thoroughly tried out. *Larix occidentalis* proved not to be immune to the disease and was a disappointment all round.

The journey was more rewarding from the point of view of the study of conifers of other kinds.

Henry visited Professor Sargent of Harvard and the Pinchots of Yale, then sailed for Europe late in October, but not for England as yet. He landed at Gibraltar in order to inspect the Spanish fir, *Abies pinsapo*. It was known to occur on three mountains. Accompanied by a gamekeeper and a donkey to carry food, he got round them all in nine days.

He went on to Italy, traversing it from south to north: Naples, Rome, Florence (where there was a good Chinese collection) and Leghorn, the port for Corsica. He went through the Corsican forests just before they were buried in snow. Thence to Algeria. "The work is rough on boots,"[298] he wrote. He did not get back to England till the New Year.

If his feelings for Elsie Brunton were an infatuation to be cured by hard exercise and change of scene, he had given himself every chance. But they met soon again. In February he took her to the theatre. Shortly afterwards he was in Ireland, staying at Dun Emer, and a letter written on the way back

suggests that he had confided in Evelyn Gleeson. She was his
first wife's friend, and evidently they had talked of Caroline.
"The dead," he wrote, "seem so terribly gone."²⁹⁹ His first
marriage now was far away and long ago.

Evelyn Gleeson had not yet found her health much improved,
and she was finding that the growing reputation of Dun Emer
created new problems. Henry, by the way, had been true to
his word as regards advertising the centre. He talked about it
and to make it known he ordered gifts from it himself, a sofa
back for Mrs. Elwes, a rug for Lady Thiselton-Dyer. The
difficulty now was to keep up with orders. There were delays
and mistakes, complaints and an atmosphere of strain. Henry's
remedy was simple: he urged Evelyn to cast care aside and take
a trip to Florence at his expense. This she could not bring
herself to do. Meanwhile, he continued to count on her
sympathy, with the self-centredness of a lover.

In March he quite lost hope. "I saw Perdita twice. She
treated me with the austerest chilliness. . . . In a word, dear
Evelyn, I have had an interesting friendship, which I have tried
to spoil by poeticising it."³⁰⁰ "I have such a delicate sentiment
for Perdita, that I would not for worlds hurt her by loving her.
She is still *quite unconscious* I am sure, that she is the heroine of
an imaginative drama."³⁰¹ Soon after that Perdita "vanished
into thin air".³⁰² Henry went to the Boat Race alone and had
a long talk with Keir Hardie.

A week later Perdita put out an olive branch. Henry had
mentioned to her his intention of buying some silk for a dress to
give his niece, May Kerley, and she offered to choose it for him.
But he knew she was busy and did not like to trouble her. His
sister Mary was in London, and the silk could be chosen by her.

In his next letter, however, the olive branch has blossomed.
They went together to see Mrs. Pat Campbell in *Hedda Gabler*.
"I write about Perdita now freely, as we have settled down
(i.e., I have; and she never was anything else) to the acquaint-
anceship and beginning of friendship. She paid for her
ticket."³⁰³ This promising state of things was maintained for
some months.

The first volume of *The Trees* was published at the end of
1906, either while Henry was still away or just after he got

back. As comment came in by degrees it was clear that it was a success. Some reviewers carped at the price, and there were criticisms of the order in which the tree genera were taken. The authors there had followed their own convenience, leaving the more difficult subjects aside to allow more time for study. As Elwes said, the index would in the end make reference easy. Nobody questioned the reliability of the information, or the value of the book. Thiselton-Dyer said, it would give "a new and much-needed impulse to arboriculture".[304]

People were at last beginning to understand that there was a need for research in forestry, as well as for technical training. In 1905 Oxford opened a school of forestry, and Dr. Schlich was transferred there from Cooper's Hill. Cambridge was about to follow suit. A readership was to be established there. Thiselton-Dyer and Colonel Prain both urged Henry to apply for it. Elwes approved, and subscribed generously to the fund. Henry hesitated because this would mean finally giving up the idea of settling in Ireland. But this hope was fading. The Department of Agriculture had, in 1904, set up a technical training centre at Parnell's old home, Avondale, and seemed unlikely to go any farther. And although his relations with Elsie Brunton were now on such a safe Platonic footing, the possibility of marriage may not have been quite absent from his mind when he finally sent in his application to the University.

Then, as Professor Sargent had come over again, Henry took him and Elwes on a whirlwind tour of Ireland, for part of which they were joined by Sir Frederick Moore of Glasnevin. In a long weekend—Thursday to Tuesday—they motored through all four provinces, visiting Castlewellan, Dereen, Fota and Mount Usher. It would imply hustling even now. Years later, in the R.H.S. *Journal*,[305] Sir Frederick recalled some incidents of the tour. He followed the others by train to Strabane, and arrived there to find a commotion. A horse in a haycart had been frightened by the car and had backed into a lamp post, which toppled over, hitting the driver on the head. He was not much hurt, but his head bled copiously and there was general consternation. Henry, the only calm person, greeted Moore with, "You are up to time. I suppose we shall soon be able to start." Another day, in the south, they had a collision. There was damage to both cars but no one hurt. Elwes was "angry, vocal and full of suggestions". In the other car sat two English tourists, silent and supercilious. Henry said, "All this is bringing us no nearer to our dinner," and suggested they walk on to Killarney. According to Moore, when others became excited, Henry was always orientally calm.

Over the years he had learnt to practise patience in adversity. Now at last everything began to go well. He was appointed to the Cambridge post. It augmented his means by £500 a year, and gave him an assured standing. The first appearance of *The Trees* had brought both its authors prestige. Henry was no longer a wanderer with a vague, speculative avocation, but a recognised authority on a subject much to the fore, and in fact an eligible suitor, even for a girl of twenty-six.

The Bruntons do not seem to have felt any misgivings about the discrepancy between his age and Elsie's. It was then more usual than now for a girl to marry a considerably older man. For one thing, widowers were more often met with. They were quite plentiful in Victorian and Edwardian society when not only infant mortality, but that of mothers was higher than today. By the autumn of 1907 Henry's courtship seems to have been generally accepted. In September Elsie sent him her photograph—"a serene and thoughtful face"—and proposed an excursion "well fortified with chaperons",[306] although they seem to have been able to dispense with these at an earlier stage. When the engagement became official is not recorded, but by Christmas it was all settled and everyone was pleased.

The engaged pair cannot have had much time together that autumn. Lady Brunton was ill, so Elsie was very much tied at home, and Henry was busier than ever before.

Volume III of *The Trees* was in the press, Volumes IV and V in preparation. There was no diminution of that work, although Henry now had an assistant, A. Bruce Jackson. He took charge of the herbarium which Henry and Elwes had by now accumulated in Cambridge Cottage at Kew. But the scheme of the work had been extended to two extra volumes, and the most difficult trees would be the last.

Besides this, and breaking new ground in his job at Cambridge, Henry had in November to go to Ireland to give evidence before a Departmental Committee on forestry. There was new activity in the Department of Agriculture. In 1906 the Conservative government had been replaced by a Liberal one, and Sir Horace Plunkett had been replaced as head of the department by a Nationalist, Mr. T. W. Russell.

The study of history would be easier if progressive or reactionary moves always followed party lines. The Nationalist, Mr. Russell, cast a cold eye on the co-operative movement nurtured by his predecessor. He lent an ear to vested interests threatened by competition from co-operative shops, and he criticised the business methods of the I.A.O.S., which presently had its subsidy withdrawn. For years the history of the co-operative movement was chequered by party politics and prejudices, but the fact that it has survived shows that the impulse behind it was after all a vital one.

In forestry, however, Mr. Russell was on the side of the angels. Under Sir Horace the Department had already started its own training centre. The first pupils of Avondale were now finishing their three-year course. The new broom immediately set up a committee on afforestation. The report which this committee produced in 1908 became the sacred scriptures of Irish forestry.

Forty-eight people gave evidence: landowners and timber merchants; representatives of county councils; representatives of industries using wood, from coach builders to bobbin makers; two railway engineers testified to the need for timber for sleepers; there were also civil servants who had to do with the administration of land. An important witness was R. Munro-Ferguson, a great Scottish landowner who had been chairman of a similar committee in England in 1902. The report Henry had sent in in 1903 on forestry regulations in France, Germany and Russia, at last saw the light. Henry himself appeared as one of five trained experts, the others being W. R. Fisher of Oxford, A. C. Forbes of Avondale, and two ex-members of the Indian Forestry Service.

Much of the evidence dealt with general problems of organisation: the acquisition of land for planting; the present position of timber production (haphazard and declining); the demand for timber (increasing and varied); and the arrangements for transporting timber from where it was grown to where it was wanted, which considerably affected the price. When at last the committee came down to the basic question of what trees to plant, it was Henry who had most to say. His advice was both detailed and revolutionary.

The other experts were somewhat vague in their recommendations. They were inclined to favour hardwoods—beech, ash, sycamore, chestnut—intermixed with larch, in spite of the risk of disease. Conifers were decidedly second best, something for higher and poorer ground.

Henry came out strongly in favour of conifers. Hardwood trees, he said, were too long term an investment. Beech takes eighty years to mature, and what the Department needed was to show quick returns. He urged them to experiment, to get away from the continental practices and try out trees from countries with mild damp climates, Douglas fir, Sitka spruce, Scotch pine and the redwoods of the American north-western coast.

What with his new academic dignity and the favourable progress of his romance he may well have been in a state of euphoria. He gave his evidence with a breezy certainty that enlivens the stuffiness of the report.

The committee was decidedly inclined to fight shy of the idea of spending money on exotic trees. Mr. Forbes had been criticised for putting a few in at Avondale. "We must have some regard for popular opinion," said one professor. "You must," Henry agreed, "but I need have none whatever. You have done the right thing at Avondale and you ought to make experiments elsewhere. As to popular opinion on the subject in Ireland it is worth nothing. People ought not to talk about things they have not studied."[307] He pointed out that there are very few truly native Irish trees. Beech, chestnut, sycamore, are all introductions. Not that he wanted them to plant anything and everything indiscriminately, as had been done at Knockboy. Someone suggested cork oak. Henry said, "If you want to try something really *recherché* there is a gutta-percha tree that grows well in Kerry."[308]

The two points he hammered home were, first that the trees must be appropriate to the climate, and secondly that they must plant for quick results. They could not afford to dally with aesthetic considerations. This sounds out of character, but he was a professional by now, immunised from mere sentiment.

"Many people look upon the establishment of forests in the same way as they look upon the establishment of an art gallery. I agree with that to a certain extent, but forestry ought to be made to pay. We know that by planting slow-growing trees the return is in the distant future. It is like investing one's money in Consols" (which was what he had done with his Chinese savings), "it may be safe, but it is quite unremunerative. Something should be done to get something above ground in Ireland. The quicker your returns the better; people will begin to see that there is something in it."[309]

His specific recommendations, listed in a memorandum appended to the report, were Sitka spruce, Douglas fir, Corsican pine, Thuya, Larch and Wellingtonia, with *Cupressus macrocarpa* and Austrian pine for shelter belts.

Of these trees, Sitka spruce represents forty to fifty per cent of planting in Ireland in recent years. The reputation of Douglas fir has waxed and waned; it is now said to be coming back to favour. Corsican pine, Japanese larch and European larch are all still planted on a limited scale. Wellingtonias and redwoods were not sufficiently superior to other timber to be worth the trouble of importing seed. *Cupressus macrocarpa* and Austrian pine never were much of a commercial proposition. The former, however, has become almost too popular in suburban gardens.

But if Henry's recommendations have not been adopted *en bloc* by later generations of foresters, his general advice to concentrate on conifers has. Nowadays the state foresters of Ireland, north and south, plant hardly five per cent deciduous trees. The demand, of course, has changed. The wood pulp industry, barely mentioned in the 1908 report, is now the foresters' largest customer. We do not want railway sleepers half so much as wallboard, chipboard, cardboard and other synthetic products. Henry hardly foresaw this as early as 1908, but he did see that if forestry was to show quick returns bulk of timber was more important than quality. He laid stress on quick returns. The taxpayer must be shown that forestry was worth while. The public had to be convinced of the importance of trees, or there would soon be no trees left.

Years were to pass before anything very much got done as a result of this committee's recommendations, but in the end Henry's advice was followed. Those who prefer the monotony of bare moors to the monotony of spruce forests, who grieve to see the clean outlines of the hills fuzzed with the saw-tooth edges of conifers, cannot but look on Augustine Henry as the chief villain of the piece.

Henry stayed with Mrs. Stopford Green over Christmas. As for Evelyn Gleeson, she sailed on December 27th for America where she was to lecture and to exhibit Dun Emer craftwork. Henry pursued her with advice and introductions. On Christmas Day he wrote to her : "It is no use your trying to shake me off, you can't do it and you won't; and you will speedily fall victim to the charms of Elsie."[310]

Far from trying to shake him off, his old friend opened her arms to his young wife, and the Henrys spent part of their honeymoon at Dun Emer.

They were married on St. Patrick's Day, March 17, 1908, quietly in a register office because of the difference in their religions, but with the blessing of an old friend of the Bruntons', the Dean of Salisbury, who conducted a short ceremony for them in the Bruntons' drawing-room. Henry, the simple-lifer, was taken aback by the number and opulence of the wedding presents. Evelyn Gleeson gave them a picture by A.E. Elwes's present was a most handsome oval table made on his own estate of a cross-cut from one tree trunk.

They went first to France and then to Ireland. The visit to Dun Emer meant a lot to Henry, in helping him to bridge the gap between his old loyalties and his new ones. In his letter of thanks afterwards he said that it had been a nice introduction to Ireland for Elsie. "She had been in Ireland before, but not the *real* Ireland."[311]

It was a completely happy marriage. So far we have only seen Henry's side of it. In the diary of Elsie's younger sister there is recorded the following conversation, which took place some five years later:

"I" (the younger sister) "said I wondered what it would be like to be married, and I thought it would be horrid not being able to get away. Elsie said one never wanted to; she used to pity Mother, never getting away from housekeeping and the servants, but after being married those things sank into such minor details.

" 'And what are the big things?' I asked.

" 'Oh, just existing together.'

" 'But while I am with Aunt Alice all the time I want to get away.'

" 'I used to feel that too; I wanted to get away altogether from life; I wanted to die. Now I am afraid to die,' she laughed with tears in her eyes, 'for fear I should not find Augustine on the other side'."[312]

Elsie always called her husband Augustine. Apart from that she did not attempt to change him.

17

At Cambridge Henry was to work harder than even he had ever done in his life, while surrounded with social and intellectual distractions of the most enticing kind. Besides organising the curriculum of the School of Forestry he had to collect funds for a building to house it. There was still the work on *The Trees*; the difficult genera which he and Elwes had postponed now had to be tackled. He also plunged into a botanical controversy on the origins of elm species, and this led him to embark on a long-term programme of research which had some far-reaching results. Cambridge was, he told Evelyn, "a powerhouse of ideas."[313] After a year there he wrote: "I do feel now as if in coming here I had burned my boats and bridges, for the work to be done here is so great there will never be time for anything else."[314]

Elsie had confided to her sister that she had doubts of her ability to run "a little house".[315] She managed admirably, however. First she had the furnishing and decoration to oversee. Then at the end of July they moved into 37 Chesterton Road. It was "clean and nice and not full of things",[316] with

9. A camp among the redwoods in the Rocky Mountains. Henry is seated second from the right.

10. Henry travelling with a donkey in Spain. "*Abies pinsapo* was known to occur on three mountains . . . he got round them all in nine days."

11. *Lilium henryi.*

fresh air from the river and a peaceful view of "cows in attitudes on Jesus Common".[317] They had two servants instead of the ten Elsie had been used to. About five hundred people formally called. Elsie called back and had three parties of about a hundred to tea.

Even before they had a home of their own the Henrys were caught up in the rush of social life that ends the academic year. There were parties and plays: *The Wasps* of Aristophanes in Greek with modern music; Milton's *Comus*, a perennial in his old university; Coquelin in *Cyrano de Bergerac*; Lady Jersey's garden party attended by royalty: "The ladies curtsied to Princess Beatrice. It is rather pretty, a nice young girl doing a curtsey," wrote Henry to Evelyn. "The day was fine and the band played and there were ices, tea and all the rest. We had two or three similar affairs."[318]

In June Henry had conferred on him the degree of M.A. *honoris causa*. It was an auspicious year all round. Elsie's father was created a baronet. Since he had been knighted under the previous Conservative administration, his family were pleased that all could see his honours were free of political taint.

Mrs. Stopford Green published the book on which she had worked so long: *The Making of Ireland and Its Undoing*. She went oftener than ever to Ireland. She began collecting funds to found a School of Irish Studies. Henry contributed twenty pounds. Was it a thank offering for his new prosperity or to appease his conscience for cutting himself off from Ireland?

The chief news from Ireland was of the theatre. Since 1904 the shell provided so generously for Yeats by his English friend Miss Horniman had been filled with talent by the brothers Fay. It staged the poetic plays of Yeats and Padraic Colum and Synge, the "Kiltartan" comedies of Lady Gregory, and more ephemeral stuff; for instance, two comedies of upper middle-class life by W. F. Casey, who forsook the theatre and ended up as editor of *The Times*. The storm over *The Playboy of the Western World* had raged in 1907. It infuriated Dublin, but was judged a masterpiece in London. Henry did not care for the image of Ireland as projected by Synge in *The Playboy*. The Erosion Commission Forestry Report, he told Evelyn, gave high praise to Irish labourers; why shouldn't their virtues be extolled? But he could not agree with a lady who said Yeats's *Cathleen ni Houlihan* was dull. "I don't think she understood it, nor anyone could who, as you say, has not 'the love of Ireland above all'."[319] This was the play of which Yeats himself was to write:

> "Did that play of mine send out
> Certain men the English shot?"[320]

The spirit of dedication to craftsmanship was also very much alive. Living organisms have a tendency to split. That summer there were changes at Dun Emer. The Yeats sisters left and set up their side of the work independently under the name of Cuala. Evelyn Gleeson continued to manage the carpet-making and tapestries, and Miss Norah FitzPatrick carried on her bookbinding in association with her. A friend, but not a business associate, was Miss Sarah Purser, whose stained-glass studio provided working facilities for many artists.

But Henry was keeping very different company. In July that year we see his social star rise to its zenith in a week-end at Lord Rayleigh's. He wrote to Evelyn Gleeson:

"He is Chancellor of the University, and Lady Rayleigh and I have been much interested in elm trees, which seed profusely at their place, Terling in Essex. She postponed my visit until I should have an opportunity of seeing her brother, Arthur Balfour. The other guests were Mr. and Mrs. Asquith and Lord Milner, with three nice young ladies of the upper ten, Venetia Stanley, Lady Gwendoline . . . and Cynthia Charteris, and two nice young men, one being Spring-Rice, Lord Monteagle's son, who is very nice and very Irish in his sympathies. It is not often that one has the chance of studying a Prime Minister and an ex-Prime Minister and it was rather interesting. I liked Arthur Balfour; he is large, strong, sensible without a particle of worry and diffuses an air of optimistic gaiety which is contagious. Asquith told good stories and is also a gay, frivolous person. Mrs. Asquith is best described as being common. She is not exactly vulgar, but she is smart. I didn't care for her. Lord Milner is a sad sort of figure. He was, however, the one most interested in forestry and took in instruction about trees like an undergraduate.

"I know you will be interested in the preceding; it all came in the way of forestry and I was keen to meet Lord Rayleigh as he is Chancellor and can ultimately help the Forestry School if he gets interested, and it is much in want of help. I looked at the two Premiers and wondered at how easy they bore the cares of Empire. In both cases it was easy to see that neither ever worried the slightest. I am convinced that a great man or woman of affairs is simply a person who works and doesn't worry."[321]

Asquith had been Prime Minister since 1906. Balfour, Prime Minister of the last government, was now Leader of the Opposition. Evidently they both had the art of relaxing on holiday. Arthur Balfour's earliest public image had been as the *arbiter elegantiarum* of the intellectual coterie known as "The Souls". Later, as Chief Secretary in Ireland, he had been nicknamed "Bloody Balfour" for his relentless policy towards Land League agitators. To him also belonged the tag about "killing Home Rule by kindness" and if this sounds contradictory, he had in fact, while discouraging hopes of independence, brought in many reforms. He had been Leader of the Conservative Party since 1891. It stood for Union and Empire and had been kept in power by anti-Home Rule votes.

Asquith had inherited the mantle of Gladstone. In 1912 he was to bring in the third Home Rule Bill, the most ill fated of all. It provoked resistance, in Ulster, and counter-resistance. All Ireland took up arms. The sister of Spring-Rice, the nice young man with Irish sympathies, helped Erskine Childers run in a cargo of guns. So from an Irish historical standpoint it was a curious collection of people to have been gathered at one house party, and it is tantalising not to know more of their conversation, but there can have been little about Ireland, or Henry would have reported it. Spring-Rice was a pianist, one of the girls a violinist. The evenings were devoted to classical music.

All the long vacation was taken up with forestry or *The Trees*. Elsie had to go home for a time; her mother was ill again. Henry took a party of students on a course of instruction. He also went on a lightning tour of Denmark, Norway and Sweden with the English Arboricultural Society. This was organised by Elwes. They did all the travelling at night and not a minute was wasted. The three countries seemed happy. "All three nations different, one can see, but all alike in the essentials, and there was no misery visible on the surface."[322]

Henry still wrote regularly to Evelyn Gleeson, but his letters dwindle to scrappy notes. Another academic year began. "I never have leisure, never time to sit down and think and muse. It is a good deal like an Antarctic expedition—one has to drive along regardless of all but the work before one."[323] But he had a staunch ally in Elsie. They were able to have guests. Evelyn Gleeson herself came for a short visit, so did Henry's niece, her pupil May Kerley. They held at their house an exhibition of Dun Emer rugs. They also fostered a small Hibernian Society of undergraduates, inviting the members for evenings.

During their engagement Henry had been worried about Elsie's health. He confided to Evelyn Gleeson: "Her father is one of those terrible workers, all the time at it, and I don't think he recognises that his children are not so strong as himself."[324] This is an outstanding example of the pot calling the kettle black.

It was well for Elsie that she had been brought up to the companionship of a man of science. She had even collected flowers in the alpine meadows on summer holidays when Sir Lauder brought his whole family to Switzerland. She spoke French and German. When they were abroad she acted as Henry's secretary, looking up references for him in libraries, keeping records, mounting specimens. Sometimes she was left to these tasks while he went on long excursions, but often she went too.

Her sister writes: "I remember her telling me of an expedition to Serbia with Augustine and how ill she was there. She caught one of the really ferocious Serbian germs and drank only milk, which afterwards she found was the worst thing she could have done, and followed in Augustine's train, perched on a mule because she could not walk." Once she remarked wistfully, "Augustine never minds where he stays, but *I* get bitten." The first time this happened she had difficulty in convincing him that her sufferings were not imaginary. His tougher hide was immune; his young wife acted as a decoy.[325]

What she found even harder to bear was being hustled past places famous in history or full of art treasures, in the relentless quest for trees. But she had married him for better or for worse, and if life with him was arduous, it was never dull.

The Serbian journey took place in the long vacation of 1909. They stopped two days in Vienna to see the Forestry Experimental Station there, before going on to Belgrade. This was then the capital of the small independent state of Serbia, as it now is of the large unified state of Yugo-Slavia, which takes in much of the old Austro-Hungarian Empire.

From Belgrade they went by steamer for five hours up the river Sava, then plunged into wild mountain country, travelling by waggon and horseback in the great forests of the Drina valley. Austria and Hungary had, the year before, annexed Serbia's neighbour, Bosnia. There was tension along the frontier, outposts on each side sniping at each other. Henry carried government credentials, and for part of the journey they had a guard.

They climbed six thousand feet to look down on a forest of *Picea omorica*, the Bosnian spruce which Elwes had gone to see in 1902. When they reached their viewpoint the entire scene was veiled in mist. Henry said merely, "What a pity!"[326]

They came by a narrow gauge railway with ninety-five tunnels to Sarajevo, and found it just like a Turkish city, with minarets and a bazaar. Carpets were made there. Elsie studied methods of manufacture for the benefit of Dun Emer, while Augustine went on an excursion with a local Professor. They went to Brod to see the oak forests of Slavonia and finally left the Balkans by way of Fiume.

Nationalist Irish readers had had their attention drawn to Hungary by Arthur Griffith in a pamphlet of 1904.[327] The subject had also been referred to more recently in the paper *Sinn Fein*, which Griffith edited. *Sinn Fein* preached national self-reliance . . . The name meant "ourselves alone". Griffith held up for imitation the pacific resistance of the Hungarians to the threat of absorption by Austria. Henry was more impressed by the grievances of the Slavs. "If the *Sinn Fein* editor knew the character of the Hungarians he would cease to talk of them, as they are aristocratic oppressors of all the

Slav peoples, who have yet to win ordinary freedom of public meetings, language, schools, etc., etc."³²⁸

They toured northern Italy, ended up in Switzerland, and so back to peaceful Cambridge, where Henry had an absorbing new interest.

Henry's interest in elm seedlings arose originally from the puzzle of how to classify the numerous varieties of elms he had to include in *The Trees*. Botanists disagreed as to how many of them could be ascribed to distinct species. He set out, as he had done years before at I-chang, to clear up a muddle over nomenclature. And as had happened before, his passion for accuracy had far-reaching practical results.

His thoughts had been ranging, as he told Evelyn Gleeson, "round weird subjects like Mendelism".³²⁹ "It is the new departure that is to explain all about heredity and variation. Mendel was a Catholic priest in Germany who started all this, he supplied the way of experiment and perhaps succeeded where even Darwin failed."³³⁰ Mendel had shown that from the crossing of two dissimilar strains one might expect progeny with the characteristics of both parents, not indiscriminately mingled but varied according to a fixed ratio. The idea, with the power it brought of breeding for definite results, was an exciting novelty then. It was soon fixed in the student mind by the limerick ending "one black and one white and two khaki".³³¹

A plant that belongs to a species ought to come true, as gardeners say, from seed. Henry set out to raise quantities of elm seedlings. "The children," he said, "will tell us about their parents."³³² The difficulty was to make sure his elms were fertilised by others of the same kind. He did not at this stage try to control the pollination himself. He looked round for places where large numbers of elms of one kind grew together. In Cambridge itself he found an avenue lined with the Huntingdon elm. He wrote to Elwes and to Kew, and to someone in the Isle of Wight. He rushed down to Exeter and gathered seed there, travelling down one night and back the next. As in the case of the western larch, the seed had to be caught at just the right stage, but the weather was kind to him. In March, April and May 1909 the sunshine broke all records. In June

Henry and his students sowed elm seed in ninety different lots. By the end of the year Henry wrote with satisfaction to Evelyn Gleeson: "I have a thousand little elms that are behaving in a very Mendelian way."[333]

In all they raised 5,300 seedlings. All those that had the same characteristics were carefully sorted out. The fact emerged that only two kinds of elms produced seedlings true to type. The conclusion was that all the elms of the British Isles originated in two main species, *Ulmus montana* and *Ulmus glabra*.

Henry summed up his experiment in a paper which he read to the Linnean Society in 1910.[334] He had secured his guide to classification. But he had more to say.

In studying hybrid trees he had been struck by the fact that they tended to be stronger and grow faster than their parents. This observation was not new in itself. Elwes, in his work for *The Trees*, had ferreted out the fact that a remarkably fine tree known as the Lucombe oak was a hybrid, self-sown in a nursery from the crossing of different oaks nearby. Elwes, also, had drawn attention to some vigorous seedlings resulting from a natural cross between Japanese and European larches at Dunkeld in Perthshire. These were the first of the Dunkeld hybrid larches, *L. eurolepsis*, now much prized by foresters. The black Italian poplar and the Huntingdon elm itself were other examples of accidental crossings producing fine trees.

The same thing had been noticed in hybrids produced by artificial pollination. A German, Johann Klotzsch, had crossed different species of pine, oak, elm and alder as long ago as 1845. More recently an American called Burbank had produced hybrid walnuts. That trees resulting from first crosses had extraordinary vigour was a generally accepted fact.

Henry asked why foresters should not go in for selective breeding? They needed fast-growing trees. Conifers were favoured on this account, but they were not the best for timber. Why not cross different species of oak or ash or walnut, to produce good timber in fewer years' time?

The suggestion at first sight seems so obvious it may appear strange that it had never been made, or if made, never taken up. But breeding trees is not as simple a matter as breeding tomatoes or roses. Henry got his elm seed in a rough-and-ready way.

Systematic pollination would mean climbing high trees not once but several times: to segregate the best flowers, to brush them with pollen, to remove coverings and let seeds mature, to cover them again before they shed, and finally to gather them. All the time a watch must be kept for the right moment to perform these operations. The weather is a hazard. The seedlings then take years to grow, and the whole process has to be repeated over generations to fix a reliable strain.

To produce such selected strains of tree seed might take centuries. There is, however, the alternative of propagating by cuttings. Even this is a slow business. The number of cuttings that can be taken from one tree is limited. Cuttings will have to be taken from those again, and so on. It does not look like a practical way of increasing stocks to the large quantities required for forestry purposes. Yet such common trees as the Lombardy poplar and the Irish yew are clones; that is, they must all have been produced vegetatively from one original stock. They descend from sports of not so very long ago.

Henry at any rate thought it worth trying to breed trees as nurserymen breed roses or tomatoes or thousands of other plants. He went on experimenting, and in another four years he had several flourishing hybrids, one of them a poplar ten feet high. These he described in an article in the *Journal* of the Irish Department of Agriculture for 1914.

Forest genetics is now a recognised research subject in England, and the work done there has followed up research in Denmark, started by Professor Syrach Larsen, who knew of Henry's experiments. There is also now in being an International Poplar Commission, with an enormous programme of experimental breeding in many countries. The organisation of this work in England was mainly due to the late T. Peace. It is being carried on in the Forestry Commission Research Branch at Alice Holt and also by the match companies.

Science is indivisible. It will not do to claim too much for the influence of any one man. Nevertheless, Henry's two papers must have stimulated thought on hybridisation. The first was translated into French and German, and the second was reprinted in the *Journal* of the North Indian Forestry Department. Both were read by an American research chemist, Ralph

H. McKee, who got backing for experiments from the Oxford
Paper Company of Maine. The state took over the work at a
later stage. An account of poplar breeding, by E. J. Schreiner,
who worked with McKee, appeared in the U.S. *Department of
Agriculture Yearbook* for 1949. Schreiner says: "Scientists
accumulated evidence on the occurrence of hybrid vigour
in crosses between tree species and varieties, but there was no
effort to create better forest trees by scientific breeding.
Augustine Henry was the first forester to do something about
it."[335]

In July, 1911, the Forestry School at Cambridge mounted
an exhibit at the Royal Agricultural Show. It was awarded a
gold medal, and was visited by the King. "He looked weak
and fagged out,"[336] Henry told Evelyn Gleeson. This was the
new king, George V. The Edwardian era had already come
to an end.

The last volume of *The Trees* came out in 1913. It had been
a jumping-off plank, then a millstone round Henry's neck, now
it was a milestone passed. It was generally praised. The
authors could congratulate themselves. Elwes in his *Memoirs*
calls it "the most complete and useful work I ever did".[337]
Henry told Evelyn Gleeson, "In the long run the work on the
book will really be of *value!*"[338]

Elwes set off immediately for Nepal, taking with him as a
present to the Maharajah, who had invited him, a pedigree
Aberdeen Angus bull.

As for Henry, soon after beginning work on *The Trees* he had
written to Evelyn Gleeson, "I shall be taken possession of by
this side."[339] It looked as if the prophecy had been fulfilled.
He now had a programme of research mapped out for years
ahead, and the School of Forestry at Cambridge was at last to
have its own building. The funds he and Elwes had collected
had been supplemented by a grant from the English Board of
Agriculture which had itself been allocated extra funds under
the Finance Act of 1910.

But the Department of Agriculture for Ireland had also been
given extra funds. It proposed to establish a Chair of Forestry
at the College of Science in Dublin. In August, 1912, Henry
wrote that if he could get the Forestry Building at Cambridge

properly equipped he could perhaps leave it to run of itself. In September he went to Dublin and had a long talk with Mr. Gill. In January he officially resigned his Cambridge post and accepted the Professorship in Dublin. The Henrys came to Dublin, "for GOOD"[340] as he wrote, on April 1, 1913.

PART THREE

"Patriotism is not enough"
Edith Cavell

Henry had helped to find Dun Emer for Evelyn Gleeson. Now she, or rather her sister, Mrs. MacCormack, found a house for him and Elsie. It was 5 Sandford Terrace (now 47 Sandford Road), Rathmines, in the early Victorian suburbs south of the Grand Canal. It was a modest address but the house itself is charming, small but not pokey, with a pleasant square hall. A strip of grass and trees, the common property of the terrace, separates it from the Ranelagh road. It has its own garden front and back, and from the back windows in those days there was a clear view to the Dublin mountains.

There are still a few people who remember this house in the Henrys' time: Elwes's oval table, the Dun Emer rugs, two pictures by A.E., one of an apple tree in the dusk, the other of a woman with two children running to her out of the sea at sunrise. Over the dining-room mantelpiece hung panels of red silk with Chinese characters in gold. On the drawing-room mantelpiece was a Tanagra figurine and two red Bohemian glass jars. There was a cottage piano in there. Elsie had friends who came to play the piano, violin and small, home-made bamboo pipes. This room was often filled with people and talk. The Henrys when they were alone sat in Augustine's study, a small room at the back lined from floor to ceiling with shelves on which the tree specimens they collected on their journeys were stored pell-mell in cardboard dress boxes.

In the garden was a walnut tree which Augustine pollinated. Elsie grew some of his Chinese plants. By the front gate they presently planted a hybrid poplar, *P.vernirubens*. It grew too big —fifty-one feet in fifteen years—and has since been half cut down. They had a gardener, a cook and a housemaid. Under Elsie the house ran on oiled wheels.

Augustine now, though extremely fit and vigorous, had

acquired an air of seniority and gone grey. He stooped a little. Young men thought of him as old. But he could outwalk all his students on excursions. He had a curious rhythmic gait which carried him through the longest march. A friend on active service observed that Chinese troops walked the same way, and no doubt he had acquired it on long collecting journeys with his coolies. Mary, the cook, in a comment recorded by Elsie, gives an amusing picture of his still youthful energy: "Isn't he like a bee? Sure isn't his skin like an egg, and all that has gone through his brain, God bless him!"[341]

Among their first guests were Mrs. Stopford Green and Elsie's younger sister, Nancy. Mrs. Green came fresh from the dignity of having an honorary D.Litt. conferred on her by Liverpool University. The students had acclaimed her by singing words of their own to that hardworked tune *The Wearing of the Green*.

Nancy Brunton in her diary gives a youthful view of the Henrys' circle. For Nancy the Irish, with their poetry and drama, their hopes and their griefs, evidently had a peculiar glamour. She notes how one evening at Sandford Terrace there sat side by side Padraic Colum and Joseph Plunkett, the outgoing and incoming editors of the *Irish Review*. This was the most literary of a number of small periodicals of nationalist sympathies. Joseph Plunkett was the son of Count Plunkett, who held a post in the National Museum and was an old friend of Evelyn Gleeson's. She had sent Henry the *Irish Review* at Cambridge, and he had complained that it was gloomy, but Nancy, who wrote poetry herself, felt a thrill at such contacts.

Plunkett took over the editorship from Colum with his friend Thomas MacDonagh, who was associated with Patrick Pearse in his Irish school, St. Enda's. A year later, Plunkett and MacDonagh, with Edward Martyn, started a theatre which was to be both more Irish than the Abbey and to put on great foreign plays, as the Gate did in after years.

Sir Roger Casement had a series of articles[342] running in the *Review*. Nancy may not have known this, as they were anonymous. He was one of her great heroes. Since he and Mrs. Green first met in London, he had added to his laurels by a mission to Peru, where he had uncovered further horrors. He had been knighted in 1911. Yet though he had done so well in the British Consular Service, he had become extremely anti-British. His articles foresaw a war with Germany, and urged Ireland to be ready to take advantage of it. He was anxious to retire from the service, and thought he might soon be invalided out. Sir Lauder Brunton had examined him and found nothing much the matter with him, but he had noted one slight sign that might indicate a lesion in the brain, and later this came to seem significant.[343] In June, 1913, Sir Roger did, after all, retire on grounds of health. Accounts of Casement are strangely contradictory. To some he was the soul of generosity and charm, to others an egocentric bore. He and Mrs. Stopford Green were as much as ever hand in glove. An older niece of hers confesses[344] that she could not endure his long tirades about Ireland, but to Nancy he seemed like one of King Arthur's knights.

A.E., just as contradictory a character, was more wholly lovable. Nancy describes him coming in and making them all laugh about George Moore. Moore's pseudo-reminiscences, *Ave et Vale*, were written, he had told A.E. "out of pure affection". A.E. had retorted, "Your affection is like a porcupine rubbing itself against one's bare legs."[345] The seer went on to hold forth on reincarnation, and peopled the countryside for Nancy with strange mystic entities, so that a day or two later in the mountains she was sure she heard supernatural bells.

The Henrys had no children of their own, but numerous children stayed at Sandford Terrace. Augustine's sister Matilda Kerley had been left a widow with a large young family, and he and Elsie interested themselves in the young Kerleys' education. His brother Tom's children also came to stay, and later on James Stephens's son and daughter. Evelyn Gleeson's nieces, now young ladies, were frequent visitors. The house was wide open to the young.

There was a dark side to living in Dublin and they soon discovered it. The long tale of the sorrows of the Irish suddenly had a new twist; the woes of the peasants were outdone by the misery of the slums. The efforts made over the years by all the various organisations already mentioned had considerably alleviated the lot of the peasants. But the misery of the country must have contributed its share to the state of the slums. An inquiry of 1913 showed 60,000 people to be living in houses unfit for habitation. Many of them must have been country born, or the children of parents who instead of emigrating moved to town. The overflow of the rural population trickled into the city and, with the poorest class already there, formed a pool of unskilled cheap labour. It was the same in all big cities. Employers drew on the pool without any stirrings of social conscience. It was accepted that human societies in the end came down to dregs.

Jim Larkin, a trade union official from Liverpool, was getting the unskilled workers to unite. The employers also united in a federation, and the conflict of interests was declared. In 1913 the clash came. The employers in the federation required their employees to resign from Larkin's union. They refused and were locked out. Other unions struck in sympathy, leading to other lock-outs. In the Henrys' first summer in Dublin thousands of people were out of work and many of them were starving.

The situation was new. It had nothing to do with the old underground agitation against England; it was part of a class struggle that was breaking out in other industrial centres. Larkin not only got the Irish workers to unite; he appealed to the British unions to help them, and food ships from Liverpool steamed up the Liffey.

The editor of *Sinn Fein* denounced Larkin as a demagogue. Yet the national movement and the labour movement soon got mixed up with each other. Intellectuals and dilettantes, whose patriotism up to now had been of a sentimental kind, suddenly woke up to the hard facts of the plight of large numbers of their fellow countrymen. The writers in *The Irish Review* expressed sympathy with the strikers, as did the more widely known writers, Yeats and Shaw. The Countess Markiewicz, an Anglo-Irish lady married to a Polish painter, helped to organise soup kitchens. When Larkin was arrested his two sons were taken in by Patrick Pearse at St. Enda's, the Irish-speaking school.

A.E. went to London and spoke up for Larkin at a meeting in the Albert Hall. On his return he found himself in hot water with his employers. The Henrys took him to lunch at Jammet's. He tapped a meringue and said pensively, "This is the best

12. *Davidia involucrata.* (*Copyright J. Downward.*)

13. *Clematis henryi.*

14. Memorial erected by the Society of Irish Foresters in a grove at the State School of Forestry at Avondale, Co. Wicklow. Beside the stone is *Hypericum patulum var. henryi*. In the background, *Pinus armandi*.

thing that has happened to me since I came back."[346] He took
Elsie to Liberty Hall, the union headquarters, where three
thousand people were getting relief. She was shocked to see the
feebleness of the unemployed. She went also to see a school
where voluntary charity provided meals for three hundred
children. The building was ruinous, and repairs were held up
by the strike. One child, called on to recite the Lord's Prayer,
began, "Our Father who worked in heaven . . ."[347]

Sir Roger Casement became concerned about school chil-
dren in the country. He adopted the school of a village called
Lettermullen and raised a fund to supply cocoa and biscuits.
When he left Ireland it was administered by his friend, Douglas
Hyde, the founder of the Gaelic League.

Elsie Henry had begun by now to keep her own record of
events, not a diary but a scrapbook of jottings and cuttings. In
the winter of 1913 she notes: "Dined with the de Montmorencys.
Capt. White was there (son of Sir George White of Ladysmith).
He is organising and drilling the 'Citizen Army' mainly
Larkin's men." On a January day she went to see them. "A
good display of 70 men drilling with sticks. Captain White has
had as many as 600 out, but this was only the picked ones for a
show drill, as he is trying to get money for boots for the men.
What is it among so many, 15,000 men out on strike?"[348]

The Lord Lieutenant and his lady, Lord and Lady Aberdeen,
earnestly tried to give a lead to useful endeavours. They came
on one occasion to learn about forestry.

Henry was lecturing to the Irish Forestry Society, in the
back premises of a teashop in St. Stephen's Green. It was, says
Elsie, "a modest little violet as societies go. A few hours
before it began a telegram arrived stating that the Lord Lieut.
would be present. Accordingly a blazing red carpet was
spread over the pavement and their Exes made a royal progress
between tea urns and buns . . . every aperture was then herm-
etically sealed as the Lord Lieut. is Very Sensitive to Draughts.
The heat was appalling and some of A.'s lantern slides melted.
. . . A. rose to the occasion and acquitted himself valiantly. He
showed the rope of bog fir." (This was rope made from the
fibres of wood dug out of the bog.) "He said it was an industry,
and one old man in Coleraine with a sign Fir Rope Maker over

N

his door still turns it out, and that it should be encouraged. At this point the L.L. politely pointed his finger at Lady A. who acknowledged it with a graceful bow."[349]

The *Irish Times* next day, while doing full justice to the glory of the Vice-regal visit, got the contents of the lecture all wrong and quoted Henry as praising the plantings by Lord De Vesci at Knockboy. Henry was obliged to write and point out that the Knockboy planting was an awful example, whereas Lord De Vesci's successful experiments were on peat bog at Abbeyleix.

In September, 1913, the Henrys went to a wonderful week-end in Ulster organised by Francis Joseph Bigger, whom Augustine had first met at the British Association meeting in Belfast. Like Yeats, Mr. Bigger had taken an old tower and furnished it. He had also discovered and reassembled the fragments of an ancient stone cross. Two of the pieces had been built into the wall of the Presbyterian church, and how Bigger got them out was his secret. He was a Presbyterian, but he had presented a stained-glass window to the Catholic church of the near-by fishing village of Ardglass, and there was to be a ceremony of unveiling, "a Gaelic demonstration" the *Irish Times* called it, though if it had any political intent, it seems to have been a gesture of good will all round.

The tower was the usual square block with a guard-room on ground level and great hall above reached by a spiral stair. It was furnished with objects of Irish workmanship of every age. There were big bronze candelabra and the walls were hung with banners. At tea on the Saturday they had home-made currant bread and oat cakes on a linen cloth. The other guests were Mrs. Green, Sir Roger Casement, and Lord Ashbourne, who was to unveil the window. He was a Gaelic revivalist whose enthusiasm was carried so far as to wear a kilt. He made a speech in Irish to the villagers afterwards, and there was a torchlight procession with pipes and drum. Then came supper with lobster, more oat-cakes and whiskey. The day ended with prayer.

Next morning almost everyone went to Mass at ten. The Henrys slipped off afterwards for a little peace. The high moment came in the afternoon. The Rosary was recited in the tower and the responses were given by the pipers whom Mr.

Bigger had stationed on the stairs. They then all marched to the church. During the unveiling ceremony the Presbyterian donor knelt on a special *prie dieu* at the altar rails.

The day ended with dancing. Late the night before the police, who were keeping a watchful eye on the proceedings, had suggested to the pipers that they might pack it up, and this regrettably had had the effect of starting the processions off afresh. "This evening," Mrs. Henry noted, "the police said nothing but stole into the guard room where the boys found them sitting sheepishly round on benches. Mr. Bigger was appealed to as to whether this might be, and Mr. Bigger came down. Before long they were processing round the room, Mr. B. with a policeman's helmet on his head and a baton in his hand, the three police solemnly after him and the pipers. Then there followed great Ulster speeches, F.J.B. (their host) demanding in stentorian tones, 'Will the sun *never* set on the Empire?' 'Never, NEVER!' was the solemn fervent response."[350]

There was still time for being innocently gay, but things were changing.

The Home Rule Bill introduced by the Liberal government under Asquith in 1912 was being opposed with determination by the Ulster Unionist party. Their leader was Sir Edward Carson, Solicitor-General for England. They had formed an army, the Ulster Volunteers, and though they were defying the law the authorities, like the Chinese Imperial Government when faced with the Boxers, took no steps to interfere.

The worst feature of this resistance—apart from the simple fact of its illegality—was that it was sectarian. The slogan, "Home Rule will be Rome Rule!" was its most forcible appeal. A month or so after the gaieties at Ardglass, Mrs. Stopford Green and Sir Roger Casement went to Ballymoney, County Antrim, to address a meeting of Protestants with a different outlook, in support of Home Rule, and in protest against the Carsonite attitude to Roman Catholics.

Staying with the Henrys on her way through Dublin Mrs. Green had admitted to them that she was anxious about this meeting but all went well. The *Irish Times* report played it down. According to this it excited little interest and the Home Rulers seemed to be a small minority. Nevertheless, the hall had been packed and Mrs. Green on a postcard spoke of "deep and sustained enthusiasm".[351] Casement wrote: "We had a *great* meeting: splendid in *every* way and Mrs. Green excelled herself."[352] He was given to superlatives, and this was his first appearance on a political platform. They both thought it had been a success, but the protest had no effect on events.

Another friend and ally of Mrs. Green's was Eoin McNeill, Professor of Ancient Irish. He had been asked by one of the papers for an article[353] on the situation in Ulster, and, after tearing up six drafts (as he told Elsie Henry), had written one on national defence. This had led to a committee being formed, a public meeting was held, and within a fortnight McNeill found himself at the head of another army of volunteers. Their aims at this stage were vague, but they, too, began drilling. McNeill spent an evening with the Henrys during November. Elsie noted in her account of it, "He hopes the Citizen army will amalgamate, when the strike is settled, and possibly the army of the north, Carson's, after Home Rule comes in."[354]

Strange as it may seem, the Irish volunteers in the south at first felt they had quite a lot in common with the northern movement. Though one army was to oppose Home Rule and the other to support it, both were refusing to be dictated to by England, and living up to the notion of self-help contained in the motto, "Ourselves alone". McNeill used to call at meetings for cheers for the Ulster Volunteers. This did not, however, always go down well. The newspapers stated that furniture was thrown about at one meeting in Cork, but McNeill himself told the Henrys that it was only the Chairman's table, which was on castors, and skated away from under him off the platform on top of the press table below.

A first cousin of Elsie's, Bea O'Brien, one Sunday joined the Citizen army on a march. "The great game of the army is to march as fast as ever it can. It is escorted by battalions of police 6 ft. 6 ins. each and in long skirted coats. The faster the army marches the hotter do the panting policemen become, and the whole joy is to give them a run for their money."[355]

The elements of farce helped to conceal from people of good will the underlying bitterness.

It was not by sheer magnetism that Professor McNeill had so rapidly recruited an army. In the background were the members of the Irish Republican Brotherhood, a secret society dating from the previous century. One of their Supreme Council, Bulmer Hobson, has told[356] how they had begun to drill, and were looking round for a respected figure to lead them in public, when McNeill's article appeared. Long before the Ulster Volunteers were formed, the I.R.B. had been planning, not for Home Rule but for uncompromising independence. They, at least, knew what they wanted. Mrs. Green and her friends were as yet unaware of their existence.

Sir Roger was fighting a private war of his own. He had been with McNeill on the platform at the meeting when the table ran away, but it was other business that had brought him to Cork. The Cunard liners had given up calling at Queenstown (now Cobh), and this meant a blow to the commerce of the south. Casement hoped to get the Hamburg-Amerika line to call instead. He thought it was all arranged, and had a public welcome laid on, when the German line backed out. Casement was certain it was the result of machinations by the British Foreign Office. But the excess of his indignation suggests that besides suffering frustration he had been injured in his vanity. He complained about the situation in the *Irish Times*, and in the *Irish Review* he writes of the affair like a man with a monomania.[357] His friends nevertheless went on taking him at face value, and respected his efforts to forward Irish interests.

In February he was again at the Henrys, "having come straight from London where he left Aunt Alice, beautifully dressed, going to lunch with Lord Haldane, who had sent for her specifically to pick her brains about Ireland and the Home Rule Bill".[358] Lord Haldane, an old friend of Mrs. Green's, was then Lord Chancellor. No wonder her admiring relations considered her a power behind the scenes!

Alice Stopford Green had never lacked self-confidence. If presently she overstepped the bounds of legality, it was because she was sure she knew what the situation required. And she had precedent for her actions.

In Ireland the atmosphere of frustration deepened through the first months of 1914. The strikes had petered out in midwinter. The Home Rule Bill was held up by an amendment proposing to partition off part of Ulster, and the argument seemed likely to go on indefinitely.

The authorities, not caring to prohibit the drilling of *all* the armies, had in December made a proclamation forbidding the import of arms. Elsie Henry pasted the cutting into her scrapbook with the indignant comment, "Ulster *has* arms." The Ulster Volunteers were believed to be getting underground support from the legitimate army. In March, serving officers at The Curragh indicated that they would not fight their fellow-countrymen in Ulster if so ordered. This incident was magnified into the "Curragh Mutiny". The Henrys, jaunting one day to Kingstown, were surprised to find two British men-of-war anchored outside the harbour. Three days later Sir Roger dropped in. He had been in Belfast on his shipping business, had found the place swarming with war correspondents of European papers, and had given all of them his views on Home Rule.

In April the Ulster Volunteers had the audacity to bring in from Germany a cargo of arms and ammunition which they landed without interference at Larne.

The Irish Volunteers now could not rest till they had guns too. It was a matter of prestige. It made no difference that they had in the meantime placed themselves at the disposal of John Redmond, leader of the Irish party in Parliament, who would not have countenanced an illegal move. Casement took the initiative and Mrs. Green backed him up. They collected subscriptions, formed a small committee, sent a man to Antwerp to buy arms. Erskine Childers and Conor O'Brien volunteered to transport them in their private yachts. There was in all this an element of boys' adventure story romance. They were "Buchaneering". None of them was clear about how the guns were to be got into the country, nor had McNeill any suggestions. That side of the scheme was efficiently taken in hand[359] by Bulmer Hobson, member of both the Volunteers and the I.R.B.

Henry had nothing to do with all this marching and counter-marching. He was fully occupied. He never at any time had more than one or two students at university level, but he lectured also to horticultural and agricultural students and took them for excursions. He advised on and supervised research work. He also lectured to outside bodies. He read to the Royal Dublin Society a paper on *Trees and their Varieties* dealing with the botanical differentiation of species and the distinction between a species and a sport. He lectured to the Archaeological Society of Louth, and to the Field Club of Belfast, on a new theme: *The History of Woods and Trees in Ireland*, showing how vegetation throws light on history and pre-history, how plant distribution reveals the sequences of geological and climatic changes, as well as the customs of men. Long perspectives had a fascination for him. Like high mountains and the ocean, the immensity of the past had in it, for him, something both awful and consoling.

In May, as the result of much letter-writing to botanists in Europe and America, a test tube of walnut pollen arrived from Portugal. Elsie notes, "Augustine procured a 20-ft. ladder and commandeered all the cabbies in the neighbourhood who carried it in solemn procession into the garden and set it up under the walnut tree."[360] Then took place the crossing of the Henrys' tree, *Juglans regia*, with *Juglans nigra*. Burbank of California had, by crossing *Juglans regia* with *Juglans californica*, produced a tree that in fifteen years grew eighty feet high. On two successive days Henry toiled up the ladder and dusted a hundred and forty stigmas with pollen and tied up the flowers in muslin bags. Within a week little fruits had formed. Alas! on May 25th there was a sharp frost, and they all fell blackened to the ground.

An American visitor had once proclaimed, standing in the Bruntons' hall: "The major blows of Fate I can withstand, it's the collateral smacks that get me down."

Major blows of fate were soon to rain on them. The Archduke had already been shot at Sarajevo. But it was still the summer. The Henrys accepted a long-standing invitation to visit some old friends of the Bruntons in Brussels. These were Professor Heger and his family, interesting because connected with the Hegers with whom Charlotte Brontë stayed. The M. Heger whom she fell in love with had thrown her letters into the waste-paper basket, but Mme Heger had rescued them, and their descendant, while visiting the Bruntons, had presented them to the British Museum.

Professor Heger was Director of the Institute of Physiology in Brussels and Professor of Physiology at the university. His daughter, Mme De Page, was the founder of the *Ecole Belge des Infirmières*, directed by Edith Cavell.

They had four days of delightful sociability, visiting forests and gardens. Elsie was proud to find Augustine being a great success with her continental friends. Someone asked him what he thought of the situation in Ireland. He replied, "Calm on the surface but a volcano underneath." But a waggish bystander said, "Are you speaking of Miss X?" and everybody laughed.[361]

Elsie went on to make some visits in England, but Augustine had to go back to Sandford Terrace before leaving again for an English Arboricultural Society meeting in Leeds. While she was at the Crums Elsie read of the guns being landed at Howth and had a letter from home. Did it surprise her? Journal entries indicate that she knew something was afoot, but not the details.

Bulmer Hobson had arranged for the landing to be done openly in broad daylight. He was less interested in the guns themselves than in the chance for a spectacular gesture. The arms would go nowhere towards a revolution; the news story would bring in funds from American sympathisers, and enable the I.R.B. to do the thing properly in the long run. Everything went without a hitch. But after it was all over the Dublin crowds jeered at the soldiers, and shots were fired, killing bystanders. Jack B. Yeats afterwards painted a dramatic picture of a shawled woman dropping a rose on the spot.

Henry's letter[362] to his wife shows that he at any rate knew nothing beforehand. All he knew was that "Aunt Alice arrived at 7 p.m. preceded by telegram," and also Miss Spring-Rice. "She was very tired—as she apparently was the lady who steered the yacht that brought the guns." He adds, "There was a nice supper for 3 although neither Mary nor I expected anyone."

The letter suggests that Henry, whatever his sympathies, had a poor opinion of the abilities of the nationalist leaders. The Ulsterman came uppermost in him. He admired Carson's efficiency. "Carson has *all* the cards and his people are disciplined. . . . The nationalists have no statesmen whatever,

no person to look ahead, no one to lead. They are not up to
Carson's form." He had opened a bottle of Graves for Mrs.
Green and Miss Spring-Rice, but his letter does not sound as if
he felt like celebrating. What would happen next was anybody's guess. Perhaps Asquith would dissolve parliament, he
wrote on July 27, 1914. What happened next was the invasion of
Belgium.

19

The war seems to have taken everyone by surprise and yet
everyone had been expecting it. Elsie's father, Sir Lauder
Brunton, said he had foreseen it fifteen years before. Articles
had been appearing in periodicals discussing what each country
should do when the time came, whether Irish interests were one
with Britain's, as Conan Doyle maintained in the *Fortnightly*, or
diametrically opposed, as Casement had said in the *Irish Review*.
But as they knew not the day nor the hour, few people had
thought out what they would do.

The proclamation against bearing arms was revoked and
young men flocked into the volunteer movements, most of
them expecting to have to repel a German invasion. Carson
cannily warned his followers not to enlist in the Regular Army
until they knew what was to happen to the Home Rule Bill.
Redmond impulsively pledged the Irish volunteers to loyalty
in a flourish of oratory. Arthur Griffith wrote in *Sinn Fein* that
if Irishmen were to defend Ireland it must be under Ireland's
flag.

The wheels within wheels of the volunteer movement have
made some historians dizzy. Redmond had certainly gone too
far. Even moderately loyal volunteers thought he had missed
a great chance to bargain. Now the Home Rule Bill was
bundled out of the way. It was, in fact, passed in September,
but its operation was indefinitely suspended.

On the Sunday after war was declared, the Henrys had
Erskine Childers to lunch to meet Mrs. Green, and Bulmer

Hobson to tea. Childers was about to leave for England. He was torn between his summons to duty and his work for the Volunteers, but, as he had shown in his novel *The Riddle of the Sands*, he had expert knowledge of the coast of Friesland, and he was going to put it at the disposal of the British Admiralty. It was three years before he again took a hand in Irish affairs. Bulmer Hobson was hon. secretary to the Volunteers, but long before the movement started he had been working in the I.R.B. to prepare for a guerilla fight against England. The war for him was something that might be turned to account. Mrs. Green denied being pro-British, but was against asking for German help. With her, feminine logic was at work. Of her two chief friends, not present, Sir Roger Casement, openly pro-German, was in America collecting money for guns. Eoin McNeill was not exactly pro-German, but felt the chance of getting German help for an Irish rising was too good to miss.

Of the ordinary volunteers, more than a few joined in order to fight England's war. Most of them meant to fight Germany if she invaded Ireland. Some only meant to resist conscription by England. A few were determined to fight for Ireland. Pearse and MacDonagh and Joseph Plunkett had ideas more fixed than Mrs. Green and her circle, but this no one suspected.

Nevertheless Mrs. Green was worried, and this, in September, is reflected in her niece's notebook: "The £1,500 privately subscribed for gun-running was to be recovered by the sale of the guns and reinvested, but the guns were never called in, they are scattered about anywhere now. The only hope of the I.V.s is in discipline."[363]

Augustine left unconcernedly for County Clare, there to assist in making a map of the geographical flora. On the way to the station he ran over his last instructions to Elsie: "Don't unlock the roller-top desk—keep all newspapers—go through all letters—be sure to change the specimens, etc., etc.—and don't worry about England, America will see to it!"[364]

Elsie became a V.A.D. She was soon a quartermaster in the College of Science female branch of the scheme of Voluntary Aid Defence, under the auspices of the St. John Ambulance. She and a botanist friend, Mrs. Wright, became interested in the possibilities of some work that had been started in Scotland, the making of surgical dressings out of sphagnum moss. This was to be Elsie's particular war work. As will be seen, it was no mean contribution, and earned her an O.B.E.

Augustine did not join any of the armies, even the St. John Ambulance Brigade. His own work fully occupied him. He figures in his wife's scrapbooks mainly as an utterer of reassuring statements and a disbeliever in rumours. He allayed a scare about signalling off the Wicklow coast, by proving that the suspicious light was the planet Venus.

When the Germans reached Brussels he wrote to Elsie from Clare: "I suppose *people* will be safe but uncomfortable with the Germans billeted on them."[365] He was thinking of the Hegers. Presently, when refugees began to arrive, the Henrys wrote through a mutual friend in neutral territory offering Professor Heger hospitality. In November they heard from him. He was in Holland. Later they learnt how he had been sent for by the Belgian Queen in exile, and how he had contrived a permit to accompany an influential patient first to Switzerland. He wrote of burning towns and long lines of homeless people. The woods they had visited in July were already cut down. But he would not leave his post. He was going back to Brussels.

Augustine's sister Mary became superintendent of a Red Cross hospital in East Grinstead. Her husband had been called up and promoted. One of the Kerley girls was nursing at St. Thomas's. Elsie's first cousin, Robert Stopford, went to Dunkirk with the Anglo-Belgian Red Cross. Her elder brother, Ted, who had just graduated in medicine, interrupted his career to join the Army. Her other brother, Stopford, was a Lieutenant on the instructional staff of the Canadian Army. Nancy was in Ireland. She had passed first of her year at a Horticultural Training College, won the R.H.S. gold medal and become an instructor in gardening. Sir Lauder Brunton, now a widower, old and frail, remained in London with his able secretary, Miss Jaffe, and asked his daughters not to risk submarines to visit him.

In December an old friend of Mrs. Green's was appointed Under-Secretary for Ireland. The Lord Lieutenant was now Lord Wimborne, the Chief Secretary was the essayist, Augustine Birrell. Mrs. Green's friend, Sir Matthew Nathan, was an Edwardian bachelor, sociable and cultured. Soon after his arrival the Henrys and Mrs. Green lunched with him at Jammet's. They found he regarded the Sinn Fein movement as serious, and he urged Mrs. Green to show herself pro-British. "You have power, use your influence for your country's good!" She tackled him on Home Rule, but he was dubious. "Who," he wondered, "would form the ruling class?"[366]

Mrs. Green was not giving up Home Rule, but she was less and less happy about the Volunteers. She tried to impress on Professor McNeill that German intervention would be disastrous. She and her niece Dorothy went to stay with Sir Matthew at the Under-Secretary's lodge in Phoenix Park, and the Henrys were invited to dinner there. Soon afterwards Sir Matthew, accompanied by Mrs. Green and Douglas Hyde, came in state to see the sphagnum moss depot.

Elwes came on a flying visit. He had cut down twenty-five acres of his own trees and was supplying the War Office with charcoal. He was also chairman of a committee to study the use of timber in aeroplanes. Henry's friend M. Hickel was in charge of timber supplies for Paris. He wrote that he had had to make appalling inroads on French forests, but hoped soon to cut deep into German ones.

The first shock of personal loss came in May, 1915, when the *Lusitania* was torpedoed. Among the drowned was Professor Heger's daughter, Madame De Page, who had been on a mission for the Red Cross. Her father and husband received permission to go to London to claim the body. Sir Lauder Brunton saw them and learned at first hand of the horrors of the Belgian invasion. They then returned again to Brussels, and it was long before there was news of them.

In the autumn Elsie went to London, partly on an errand for the St. John Ambulance and partly for medical advice; she had strained her heart. While she was resting at her father's house, the news came that Ted Brunton had been killed at the battle of Loos. Elsie's being with her father at that time was the one small mercy vouchsafed to them. The letters of condolence they received almost all referred to the writers' own losses. They had no monopoly of grief. Only fragments of Augustine's letters have been preserved.[367] In one he writes of the antiquity of the cedars of Lebanon, and of some rites

still practised in connection with them. In another he refers to
a library book he had picked at random, describing the liberal
and humane outlook of German universities in the mid-
nineteenth century. He was calling on antiquity and history
to help him preserve a sense of proportion. No one now could
doubt the ruthlessness of the enemy. News came that, for
helping British soldiers to evade capture, Edith Cavell had
been shot.

A bad Zeppelin raid on London proved almost a welcome diversion. Elsie's brother Stopford came over from
Canada on compassionate leave with his Canadian wife.
Before returning they stayed with the Henrys in Dublin. Mrs.
Stopford Brunton studied the process of making sphagnum
moss dressings. The Central Depot for Ireland was at the
College of Science. The Marchioness of Waterford had
organised the country-wide collection of sphagnum by volunteers. It was an immense and tedious labour, but the dressings
were greatly in demand. Under Elsie's sister-in-law the work
was now to begin in Canada.

Augustine was investigating the value of Japanese larch as
a timber tree, and writing a monograph on larch. His best
hybrid poplar, *P. generosa*, had been acquired by Hilliers'
nurseries, and is still in their catalogue. Just before Easter,
1916, he went to London, to stay with Mrs. Green and work
at Kew. She wrote they had been "Darby and Joaning" in
the gardens.

Elsie and her friend Mrs. Wright spent Easter at Courtown
Harbour, a charming seaside village. The weather was perfect.
Mrs. Green in London on Easter Monday wrote of summer
plans and suggested they share a house for a holiday.

The failure of the post to arrive on Tuesday morning was the
first intimation of anything unusual. Vague, alarming rumours
were going round. On the train to Dublin, Elsie and Mrs.
Wright met a friend who told them the Sinn Feiners were up
in arms, and had seized the General Post Office. The train
was diverted to Harcourt Street from Westland Row, because
the station-master there had been shot. They did not know
how they were to get home, but Mrs. Wright's husband turned
up at the last station but one, with a car.

Life then for two or three days became completely disjointed. Nobody could understand what was happening. The V.A.D. supposed they ought to go on duty, but when someone succeeded in telephoning the Viceregal Lodge for orders they were told to do nothing and above all not wear uniform. Meanwhile the Countess Markiewicz was seen in St. Stephen's Green, a cigarette in her mouth and a pistol in each hand.

Next day, however, a Red Cross hospital opened at the headquarters in Merrion Square. The depot had an urgent request for dressings. Elsie and Mrs. Wright, at some risk to themselves, carried round a hamper-full from the college just round the corner. The sun shone and birds sang. Smoke hung over Sackville Street (O'Connell Street) to the north. Soldiers lay behind barricades of surrealistically assembled odds and ends. There were snipers on the roofs. At the Red Cross headquarters the packing room had become an operating theatre. A boy lay dying. There were several casualties. Some of the dead could not be identified, and there was a problem of where to bury them.

The only news from outside came in English papers which the troops brought over. Soldiers were being rushed across and no civilian could hope to get on a boat. No one knew what was happening up and down the country. Elsie's sister was in Limerick; A.E. somewhere in the west; Dorothy Stopford had been staying with Sir Matthew Nathan at the Lodge in the Park. Rumour said Sir Roger Casement had been arrested in Kerry. Mr. Sheehy Skeffington, while trying to stop people looting, had been arrested and was subsequently shot.

The young English soldiers arrived thinking they were in France. The young Sinn Feiners, many of them, had turned out thinking it was only a routine Bank Holiday parade.

Food suddenly ran short and there was a rush to buy up stores. The Sinn Feiners commandeered provisions, but signed meticulously for everything they took. Elsie's milkman had receipts for nineteen gallons of milk.

There was no news from Augustine till the Saturday. Then a telegram arrived to say he had landed and would be home next morning. His week had mainly been spent standing in queues to obtain permits, and he needed one more to get from Kingstown to Dublin.

Augustine as usual kept calm. He had decided in his own mind that Elsie would be safe in Courtown as she would not be allowed to go back to Dublin. He had written her a letter in duplicate, one to each address, in which he said: "Aunt Alice was much perturbed, but I remained extremely cool, mainly because there was nothing to do. I think the number of fools is too great in this world."[368]

In the following week order began to be restored. A letter arrived from Nancy. A.E. returned from County Clare, having walked most of the way. Dorothy Stopford was safe with friends. Sir Matthew Nathan had gone on the Monday to Dublin Castle and found himself imprisoned there. A policeman, closing the gate behind him, had been shot dead. But Sir Matthew had telephoned his wife and she and their guests had escaped by a roundabout way in cars. Everyone had stories to tell. Typical anecdotes were of the honesty of both soldiers and Sinn Feiners. A lost wallet had been restored by the military after passing through several hands. The Sinn Feiners had occupied a hen run and never taken a single egg.

The pillar boxes had been overflowing with uncollected letters. Mail a week old now began to be delivered, and Augustine had a letter asking urgently for a supply of tetanus serum for his brother who had had an accident in Belfast. He hurried off there. Fortunately serum had been obtained and his brother was safe.

While the general public were still preoccupied with getting back to normal and catching up on news, there began to appear, day after day, in the newspapers the announcements of executions. Elsie pasted the cuttings into her scrapbooks without comment. The ringleaders were a mere handful of obstinate men. They had counted on more help than they received from Germany. They had expected that volunteers all over the country would rise in their support. To some extent they had miscalculated, but they had also convinced themselves of the necessity for an immediate gesture, and had talked in terms of a blood sacrifice. Did they really look on themselves as a suicide squad? The Henrys had a story, merely at third hand, from some one who had talked to the leaders in the G.P.O. and gathered that they believed they would, if they surrendered, rank under international law as prisoners-of-war. Whatever they inwardly thought, they did risk their lives and died bravely. The effect was, as Pearse had foreseen, to inspire others. Long after an independent government was established in Ireland it was difficult to stop young men, brought up on the heroic legend, from shooting policemen and others who in their eyes represented the hereditary English foe.

The men who were executed were mourned by far more people than had shared their convictions. They came from every walk of life, gentlemen and scholars, shopkeepers and workers. They all had friends and family connections. It was horrifying to find that such a fate could overtake people one knew. Joseph Plunkett was in the second batch to die. Eoin McNeill had tried to stop the rising but did not shirk responsibility for it. He was sentenced to penal servitude for life. Bulmer Hobson escaped. He had been known to disapprove of a premature attempt and had been kidnapped and kept out of the way.

Sir Roger Casement was tried as a traitor in London, in an atmosphere of intense prejudice and mob hate. Copies of alleged diaries revealing him as a homosexual—an imputation infinitely more shocking then than now—were discreetly circulated by the authorities, apparently in a deliberate effort to alienate sympathy, and with a view to placating American public opinion. It required courage to take his side, but his friends in general stood by him, and Mrs. Green in particular used all the influence she could. Sir Lauder Brunton wrote[369] that he could give evidence in support of a plea of insanity, but this plea was not made. Sir Roger *had* meant to try to stop this ill-timed rising, but he had been in Germany for the purpose of getting German support. He was condemned as a traitor and hanged.

Sir Lauder's offer is the only reference to the matter in Elsie Henry's scrapbook. It looks as if she and Augustine wrote Sir Roger off as insane, but they had valued his friendship and the tragedy must have affected them.

Elsie felt much sympathy for Sir Matthew Nathan. By chance he had been in sole charge at the outbreak of the rising, as the Lord Lieutenant and Chief Secretary were both away. He had refused to be alarmist, and had been caught unprepared. After he had resigned, Elsie wrote expressing her regret. He replied gracefully that it was "moss to the wound". Urbanity must with him have been an ingrained habit.

Sir Lauder died later in 1916. There is a gap in the series of scrapbooks, and when the record resumes it is less dramatic. Henry went to London in May 1917 to deliver three public lectures, but he had a bad attack of malaria, and his script had to be read by someone else. The lectures dealt with the advantages of planting trees in water-catchment areas. They were published in book form after the war as *Forests, Woods and Trees in Relation to Hygiene*.[370] The title has no general appeal and the contents though admirable are dull.

In March, 1918, he gave, under the auspices of the Dundalk Chamber of Commerce, a lecture which became a landmark in the history of Irish forestry.[371] Though he said nothing new, he summed up everything there was to be said about what had been done up to then and should be aimed at in future.

The Departmental Committee of 1908 had recommended the state acquisition of 200,000 acres of woodlands in addition to the 300,000 acres that then existed; had hoped that another 500,000 acres would be planted by private owners and County Councils, and that in eighty years Ireland would have 1,000,000 acres of forests, the area deemed by economists appropriate to the country's needs. By 1918 very little of this programme had been carried out. About 15,000 acres of woodlands and 8,000 acres of waste land had been acquired by the Department, and 580 acres by five different county councils. Since the outbreak of war, trees throughout the country had been steadily cut down.

Henry laid down as principles that (1) Planting for timber, which must be done on a large scale and a long term plan, was a job for the state; (2) County Councils should undertake planting for shelter and ornament, and encourage private individuals and associations to do so by grants.

At the time his words seemed to fall on empty air. The war dragged on, and the political wrangling in Ireland also seemed interminable. No constructive planning was possible.

In the bitter spring of early 1917 James Stephens, who had brought his family to Dublin from Paris, caught pneumonia.

o

The Henrys took his two children for a month. There is a touching entry in the scrapbook, among much bleak news of war and politics, like a glimpse through a window of a fire-lit circle:

"This month has given the children a sense of care, interest and affection. Last night at supper we had sugar with their oranges, for the first time, and it was a great fête, and Augustine was ladling it out, and we were playing Lolo proverbs on the pattern of 'singing comes from the mouths of boys and girls'. We said, 'Singing and dancing come from Iris,' 'Great acting comes from Seamus,' 'Sugar comes from Dr. Henry,' and someone asked 'What comes from Aunt Elsie?' Straight as a flash Sonny replied, 'Love comes from Aunt Elsie.' "[372]

In 1917, in deference to American public opinion, the Irish political prisoners were released. Lloyd George called a convention of representative Irishmen to try and get agreement on some definite proposal. Erskine Childers came back to Ireland to act as Secretary. But the attempt only showed up the conflict of opinions and the extent to which rifts had deepened.

Early in 1918 Canadian troops arrived in France, and with them Elsie's second brother. Her heart now was with friends on many fronts. The scrapbooks contain more news cuttings and fewer notes. Allenby entered Jerusalem. Peace was made with the Ukraine. Then a new German offensive was launched on the Somme.

The decision was taken to impose conscription on Ireland. In the workings of the official mind it seemed a good idea to remove from the country all the able-bodied men of military age, besides its being just to treat them on a level with the British. The effect was to unite all the anti-British elements in Ireland and bring in many who had been indifferent. If a man had to fight anyway, he preferred to defend his own ground with his own fellow-countrymen. What did an Irish countryman care about the war's wider issues?

Augustine, startled out of his detachment, wrote in April, 1918, to his sister Mary: "The peasants and labourers of Ireland are inflammable material, who are now led by skilful leaders, backed up by the late Insurrection, by song, ballads and what passes for history, and by a literature, and they are out, or will be out soon—if conscription is imposed. That is my reading. These insane quarrels and misunderstandings, based on hatred, are bound to have a bad end."[373]

At last the war news began to be consistently better, and there was good news, too, of friends. Henry's niece Gertie Kerley was mentioned in dispatches. Elsie received an account of her cousin Robert Stopford's heroic work with his ambulance unit and of his several narrow escapes. Early in October she went to London with her sister, Nancy, who was applying for work in connection with War Graves gardens. They were joined by their brother Stopford and had a joyful reunion, went to theatres and saw the sights, dined out and had real ice-cream. The whole of Trafalgar Square was given up to a replica of the ruins of Rheims. At night it was lighted up!

When they went to Euston for the mail train home they found it was cancelled. On the previous day the regular mail boat, the *Leinster*, had been sunk. It had been mistaken for a troop-ship. Over four hundred passengers were drowned. When they crossed next day, escorted by an airship and destroyer and wearing life jackets, they saw a buoy with a black flag marking the spot and an old rusty ship on guard.

The king of Portugal came to Ireland and visited the Sphagnum Moss Depot. Its output now approached a million dressings, but this was far outdone by its foster children, the Canadian centres, with their target of twenty million, and from there the work had spread to the United States. At last it was no longer needed, the war was over.

The depot closed for good on December 18th. On the same morning Elsie learnt that she was to be awarded the O.B.E., and a postcard came from Professor Heger, signed by all his family, the first intimation since 1915 that they were all alive.

The Henrys spent their first Christmas of peace in London, "our first real honeymoon trip since 1914". From Sir David Prain, Director of Kew, came an invitation to lunch on Christmas Day. "Dear Mrs. Henry, would you and Dr. Henry like to do a Darby and Joan walk in the garden on Xmas morning? It is the one day in the year that it is closed."[374]

20

After the war a General Election was held. The Sinn Fein party won most of the Irish seats, announced that it had a mandate from the Irish people and set up an Irish government, the first Dail Eireann. So the last fight began.

Mrs. Green had once said, "There isn't often much you can do, but you can choose which side you will be on."[375] In this case it was not easy. The new government's first statement of policy did not inspire confidence. Socialist doctrines, such as state ownership of property, found their way in through the influence of relics of the Citizen Army. They were never really intended and later conveniently forgotten. What with this and their determination to use physical force, the new leaders had little sympathy from Henry. On the other hand, when a blackguard auxiliary force arrived to supplement the Regular Army and police, the admiration Henry had once felt for "the beloved red coats" could not be extended to the Black and Tans.

The Henrys remained uncommitted. Mrs. Green, now over seventy, chose the Irish side. She sold her London house and took one in Stephen's Green. Her house became a place where journalists and other legitimate enquirers could make contacts. Her old friends Professor McNeill and Count Plunkett were Ministers in the new Dail. Mrs. Green was no longer in their inner councils. She recoiled from physical force. With Douglas Hyde, who had founded the Gaelic League, she pleaded in vain for Ireland's case to be submitted to international arbitration. But she was suspect to the British authorities. More than once her house was searched. She proudly preserved the marks that the Black and Tans made with their knuckle-dusters on her Georgian mahogany hall door.

In London her niece Edith Stopford tried as secretary of the "Peace with Ireland Council" to sift truth from propaganda and to help people who got arrested by mistake. Her other niece, Dorothy, who had run the gauntlet of the rebels in 1916,

took a medical degree in Dublin and went as dispensary doctor
to a part of Cork where the fighting was fiercest.

In 1921 the Treaty was made with Britain, on terms that
allowed part of Ulster to opt out of the Free State. Mrs. Green
was among those who assented to this solution. She became
one of the four women members of the first Senate of the new
Free State. Most people welcomed peace. Some thought no
lasting peace could be founded on this compromise. Erskine
Childers was one who chose the side of continued resistance.
His execution shocked public opinion, but there was little
mercy shown by either side. Dorothy Stopford also sided with
the extremists, yet visited her aunt's house. "Though I have
argued with her, she remains fond of me and looks on this as a
haven of refuge,"[376] wrote Mrs. Green to Elsie Henry. Such
were the times now called "The Troubles", a word that
evades judgment.

Strictly speaking, the civil war began only after the Treaty,
but to the ordinary citizen with friends in all camps it amounted
to that from the first. Fires, explosions, breakdown of communications, curfew, raids, became the commonplaces of daily life.
The strangest thing was the instinct people had to preserve
a normal façade. Those like the Henrys, who had lost hope of
influencing events, did their best to ignore them. During
1919–20 Henry contributed to the proceedings of the Royal
Irish Academy three papers based on extensive research.[377] In
1926 he wrote a pamphlet on Irish Forestry for a series Mrs.
Green was bringing out for circulation through Sinn Fein
clubs.[378] In 1922 he summed up, in the *Quarterly Journal of
Forestry*, his findings on *The Western Larch in Cultivation*, the
sequel to his odyssey of 1906. The College of Science was
occupied by Free State troops and closed for some months, but
he still had his horticultural and agricultural classes. When, in
1926, the college was merged in the National University, his
appointment was renewed.

At least the world outside was returning to sanity and it was
possible to get away for a temporary respite. The British
Association met at Bournemouth in 1919, at Cardiff in 1920.
Henry contributed papers on The Afforestation of Water
Catchment Areas and The Artificial Production of Vigorous
Trees. In the spring of 1921 the Henrys joined the Hegers in

Paris, and met again M. Hickel and M. De Vilmorin. In 1922 they went to stay with Vicary Gibbs, a friend who had not let himself be dropped when the work on *The Trees* was finished. From this lovely home "partly Queen Anne, partly Charles II, with acres of lovely gardens" all at peace, Elsie Henry wrote to her sister this account:

"We left Dublin on Thursday night, but couldn't get to Westland Row because of the ambushes, but got a taxi to drive us to Kingstown, and were held up twice by Free State troops. Our poor taxi-man belonging to a large garage had had one cab taken from him that morning by Irregulars, and all his money, amounting to £6, stolen off his person. Today's papers say the Four Courts have been entirely blown up in one final terrific explosion and Rory O'Connor and his crowd surrendered. The buildings are destroyed, and all the documents, historic and otherwise, in them. I rather wish we hadn't come away. The cable between England and Ireland has been cut and no letters are going either way because there *is* no postal service. Bullets were buzzing round College Green and Dame Street on Thursday morning when I was down there. I saw Aunt Lily, Aunt Alice, Edie and Alice on Thursday morning and they were all right. But I do feel anxious now, being entirely cut off, and wish I'd stayed and let A. come over alone. The maids will be all right, probably, at Sandford Terrace, it is such a backwater, unless wholesale looting or incendiarism begins. The only thing to be feared is food shortage, but as the Four Courts have fallen the Free State may get control. A. crossed Leeson Street Bridge on Wednesday ten minutes after a bomb was thrown on the bridge which killed four Free State soldiers."[379]

But Henry all this time was bent on studying the geographical distribution of the Corsican pine and the European larch, and later that year he and Elsie went off to Poland to see trees in the Carpathian mountains.

In May, 1923, the extreme republicans recognised that the country was not behind them as it had been behind Sinn Fein, and many, though not all, laid down their arms.

The boundary between Northern Ireland and the Free State was fixed in 1924, by two old friends of Henry's under an outside chairman. Eoin McNeill represented the Free State and Joseph Fisher the North. It was a recognition of an incompatibility of outlook that went far back in history, through the Industrial Revolution to the plantations of James I. Henry could not but grieve to see the country of his boyhood ringed off from the part of Ireland where he had cast his own lot. But he did not lose touch with east Antrim. Every year he went to stay with his brother Tom, who had moved from Tyanee to a better house not far away. This other house, Rasharkin, stands on a windy eminence, and the protection it gets from a double row of close-planted Thuyas exemplifies Augustine Henry's teaching on the advantages of shelter belts.

The new legislators in Dublin and Belfast settled down to weave the destinies of the new Ireland. It is interesting to record that Evelyn Gleeson and her workers of Dun Emer Industries wove the carpets for the new home of Dail Eireann.

Great Britain in 1919 appointed a Forestry Commission under which advance has been rapid. The pattern of teaching and research has altered. Self-governing Dominions now train their own foresters. In the nineteen-thirties the school at Cambridge was found to be redundant and closed. But the experience of two wars has brought home the lesson of the importance of timber reserves, and the need is felt—more strongly than in Henry's and Elwes's time—for forest parks as places of relief from the spread of towns and the rush of urban life.

The Forestry Commission had no time to do much in Ireland. Its responsibility there ended in 1922. An article by Henry in the quarterly *Studies*[380] for 1924 shows that Irish woodlands were in a poor way indeed. Some 10,000 acres of the best had been cut during the war. There remained something under 300,000 acres, mostly in private hands. The Free State government disposed of about 25,000 acres for afforestation, the Northern government had 4,000, of which only 700 had been planted. At present the Republic is planting 25,000 acres and the North 5,000 every year.

Both the new governments took an interest in forestry from the first, but progress was slow, if steady, till it was halted by the Second World War. Since then it has been tremendously accelerated. A report of the Food and Agriculture Organisation of the United Nations corroborated the 1908 estimate of the country's need for a million acres of trees. Ireland as a whole is still only halfway to that target, but if planting at present rates is kept up it will be achieved in this century.

Henry was the prophet of forestry in Ireland and the forests are to keep his memory green. In 1951 a grove at Avondale Forest School was dedicated to him and a memorial stone erected there. In Northern Ireland, the Forestry Department of the Ministry of Agriculture is now considering possible sites for an ornamental forest park, which is to bear his name.

Inscribed on the flyleaf of a notebook Henry was using in 1925 are the words of Edith Cavell: "Patriotism is not enough. I must have no hatred or bitterness against anyone." In this spirit he lived out his last decade.

Internationally he had a unique position in that everywhere he had travelled he had made personal friendships which lasted. He was consulted by tree lovers and botanists all over the world, and he put them in touch with each other. He was a member or honorary member of societies in France, Belgium, Finland, Czechoslovakia and Poland, besides being on the Council of the Royal Arboricultural Society of England and on the Scientific Committee of the Royal Horticultural Society. In Ireland he was on the Councils of the Royal Dublin Society and the Royal Irish Academy.

In addition to the honours and degrees already mentioned, he was awarded in 1923 the Silver Medal of the Société Nationale d'Acclimatation de France, and in 1929 he received a distinction from China. The Institute of Peking dedicated to him its second collection of *Icones Plantarum Sinicarum*, a series of folios of plant drawings, each prefaced with a tribute to an outstanding botanist. The first dedication had been to Professor Sargent. The wording, a copy of which has been supplied by the Academy of Science, Peking, runs:

"To Augustine Henry, through whose assiduous botanical exploration of Central and South Western China, the knowledge of our flora has been greatly extended."

After Henry's death, Mrs. Henry learned from Sir John Pratt's book, *China and Britain*, that a wing of the Fan Memorial

Institute of Botany at Peking had been dedicated to him, with this same inscription. Sad to say, after the many changes that have since taken place in China, all trace of this has disappeared.

Henry worked hard to the last. He rose every morning at six to deal with his huge correspondence, punctiliously answering every letter from friend or stranger. When he took students for excursions they were expected to appear at eight, and he could still, when approaching seventy, outwalk most younger men. In addition to his regular work, he collected information for a revised edition of *The Trees*, which unfortunately he did not live to bring out.

Inevitably these years were saddened by the loss of old friends. Elwes died in 1922, Professor Heger in 1925, Professor Sargent in 1927, and Mrs. Stopford Green in 1929. These years, too, saw the break-up of many great estates he had known, and the fall of noble trees. Yet there were many people whose friendship still brought happiness: Evelyn Gleeson and her family; Dr. Douglas Hyde; and a host of young relations—Kerleys, Crums, Henrys and Stopfords—kept him and Elsie alive to the interests of the rising generations. He and Elsie gave delightful parties, blending professors, poets, artists and foresters with the utmost success. They never forgot how to be innocently gay.

They went on travelling. Early in the 1920s they went on a forestry trip to Poland. Later the Engadine became a favourite place for more restful holidays. In 1927 they joined a small botanical congress at Gap in Provence. The only other foreign members were three Flemings. Henry wrote to Evelyn Gleeson that he and Elsie represented Ireland, "the whole of Ireland, which, as a 'botanical province' is as yet undivided."[381] The Provençals and Flemings, like the Basques and the far-off Lolos, all had problems of race and language akin to Ireland's, and how much he liked them all!

Mrs. Henry gave 500 francs for the restoration of a valuable herbarium which had deteriorated in the museum of Gap. This was only one of numerous benefactions. In these years Henry distributed batches of his duplicate specimens to various institutions, either as gifts or at nominal prices. The National Museum of Wales at Cardiff received about 2,500 and 2,000 went to the Imperial (now Commonwealth) Forestry Institute at Oxford.

In his last years Henry amassed cuttings and jottings on endless side-issues of forestry and marginal studies. Archaeology especially fascinated him. He gave rein to a collector's passion for the accumulation of petty items. The trees began somewhat to obscure the wood. As the end drew near his tremendous mental powers began to fail. He was distressed to find that he could no longer rely on his memory. Resolute to the last, he attempted to discipline it, hiding things which he would then attempt in vain to find again. This painful phase lasted a year or more, but his friends still thought of him as active, and his death, after a two-weeks' illness, on March 23, 1930, took most people by surprise. He was buried with the rites of the Roman Catholic Church at Dean's Grange, Dublin. An attendance of over a hundred and twenty people is recorded, of all persuasions and politics. There may have been many more. It was an end like that of Browning's Grammarian:

"This high man with a great thing to pursue
Dies ere he knows it."[382]

But though Henry had the spirit of dedication to learning, his was never a one-track mind. On the eve of his last Christmas but one he had written to his lifelong friend, Evelyn Gleeson: "One wants a thousand years to take in all the things that one ought to be interested in."[383]

Henry left his own private collection of tree specimens lying in some confusion. There were about ten thousand of them, in loose covers with temporary labels, in a room at the College of Science. Mrs. Henry, aware of their value, single-handed tackled the appalling task of sorting them out into species and genera. She herself devised a system of arrangement, provided permanent covers and rewrote all the labels. This immense labour of love took her eight years. She then made over the whole, by deed of gift, to the National Botanic Gardens, Glasnevin, Dublin, where it now forms the Augustine Henry Forestry Herbarium.

A catalogue was still required, and this Mrs. Henry could

not undertake herself, but she placed it in competent hands. It took another four years, and unfortunately she did not live to see it completed. Shortly after her death this task too was accomplished, through the devoted efforts of the Director of the Gardens, Dr. T. J. Walsh.

In 1957, almost exactly on the date of the centenary of Augustine Henry's birth, a tablet in honour of Mrs. Henry was placed in the Herbarium, which thus usefully commemorates them both, in a way they would both have liked.

SOURCES AND REFERENCES

INTRODUCTION

1. Letter of 20 March, 1885 (Kew).
2. Letter to Miss Gleeson, 26 March, 1885.
3. Letter to Miss Gleeson, 25 May, 1897.
4. Letter to Miss Gleeson, 5 June, 1900.
5. Letter to Miss Gleeson, 1 July, 1899.
6. The late Dr. R. I. Best quotes this in a letter to Mrs. James Smith, in author's possession.
7. Letter from Henry to Miss Gleeson, 9 September, 1901.
8. Notebook of Mrs. Alice Henry in possession of Dr. Kerley.

CHAPTER 1

9. Letter to Miss Gleeson, 8 February, 1899.
10. *Ibid.*
11. *Ibid.*
12. Letter to Miss Gleeson, 20 February, 1897.
13. Letter to Miss Gleeson, 18 October, 1901.
14. Letter to author from Miss Elsie Patton.
15. Letter to Miss Gleeson, 31 May, 1900.
16. Letter to Miss Gleeson, 10 January, 1879.

CHAPTER 2

17. *These From the Land of Sinim*, 1901.
18. Notebook of Mrs. Alice Henry in possession of Dr. Kerley.
19. Undated letter to Hosea B. Morse, probably after 1895 (Kew).
20. Letter to Thistleton-Dyer, 7 September, 1885 (Kew).
21. Letter to Miss Gleeson, 8 February, 1899.

22. Notebook of Mrs. Alice Henry in possession of Dr. Kerley.

Chapter 3

23. Letter to Thistleton-Dyer, 13 April, 1888 (Kew).
24. *Kew Bulletin*, 1889. Original letter of 29 June, 1888.
25. E. H. Wilson, *A Naturalist in Western China*.
26. *Kew Bulletin*, 1889. Original letter of 29 June, 1888.
27. Notebook of Mrs. Alice Henry in possession of Dr. Kerley.
28. *Kew Bulletin*, 1889. Original letter of 29 June, 1888.
29. *Kew Bulletin*, No. 33, p. 225, 1889.
30. Letter to Mrs. Kruming.
31. Letter to Thistleton-Dyer, 30 April, 1897 (Kew).
32. See letters to Thistleton-Dyer of 29 June, and 17 July, 1888 (Kew). Also letters to Sargent, 31 May, 1894, 30 October, 1894 (Arnold Arboretum).
33. Letter to Thistleton-Dyer, 29 June, 1893 (Kew).
34. Letters to Thistleton-Dyer, 21 January, 1889 and 12 March, 1889 (Kew).
35. Letter to Thistleton-Dyer, 7 December, 1888 (Kew).
36. Notebook of Mrs. Alice Henry in possession of Dr. Kerley.
37. Letter to Thistleton-Dyer, 9 August, 1889 (Kew).

Chapter 4

38. Notebook of Mrs. Alice Henry in possession of Dr. Kerley.
39. *Ibid.*
40. *Kew Bulletin*, 1891, reprinted from *Chinese Customs Publications*, No. 16, 1891.
41. Cutting, found among the letters to Miss Gleeson, from the *Evening Herald*, Dublin, undated.
42. Letters to Miss Gleeson.
43. Letter to Thistleton-Dyer, 7 March, 1891 (Kew).
44. Letters to Miss Gleeson, 5 March, 1896, 29 August, 1896.
45. See letter to Thistleton-Dyer, 24 October, 1891 (Kew).

CHAPTER 5

46. Bret Harte: *Plain Language from Truthful James*, Poems, 1870.
47. *These From the Land of Sinim*, 1901.
48. Letter to Thistleton-Dyer, 4 August, 1892 (Kew).
49. Letter to Thistleton-Dyer, 24 October, 1891 (Kew).
50. See letter to Miss Gleeson, 8 August, 1903, and also letter to C. F. Millspaugh, 12 January, 1923, in the Natural History Museum, Chicago.
51. Letter to Thistleton-Dyer, 15 October, 1892 (Kew).
52. Sir Alexander Hosie (he was knighted for his services). Earlier, as British Consul at Chungking, he had investigated the production of insect white-wax, an export of Szech-wan.
53. See letters to Thistleton-Dyer of 18 November, 1892, and 17 July, 1894 (Kew). Also notebook of Mrs. Alice Henry in possession of Dr. Kerley.
54. Letter to Thistleton-Dyer, 18 November, 1892 (Kew).
55. Letter to Miss Gleeson, 8 December, 1897.
56. Notebook of Mrs. Alice Henry in possession of Dr. Kerley.
57. *Ibid.*
58. Letter to Sargent, 31 May, 1894 (Arnold Arboretum).
59. Letter to Thistleton-Dyer, 17 July, 1894 (Kew).
60. See letters to Sargent, 31 May, 1894, and 30 October, 1894 (Arnold Arboretum).
61. Letter to Miss Gleeson, 5 March, 1896.
62. I am indebted to Mr. Padraic Colum for this reminiscence, and for reference to A.E.'s poem.
63. Letter to Sargent, 30 October, 1894 (Arnold Arboretum).

CHAPTER 6

64. Notebook of Mrs. Alice Henry in possession of Dr. Kerley.
65. Letter to Miss Gleeson, 30 August, 1905.
66. Letter to Thistleton-Dyer, 15 October, 1892 (Kew).

67. See Janet Dunbar: *Mrs. G.B.S.—A Biographical Portrait of Charlotte Shaw*, 1963.
68. *Ibid.*
69. Letter to Miss Gleeson, 9 November, 1895.
70. Letter to Miss Gleeson, 4 August, 1896.
71. Letter to Miss Gleeson, 14 November, 1896.
72. Letter to Miss Gleeson, 17 October, 1902. The other lady was Miss Norah Fitzpatrick. See Chapter 13.
73. Of the *American Druggist*.
74. Letter to Miss Gleeson, 15 November, 1895.
75. Letter to Miss Gleeson, 22 September, 1896.

CHAPTER 7

76. See letter to Thistleton-Dyer, dated 2 March, 1895, a mistake for 1896 (Kew).
77. Letter to Thistleton-Dyer, 14 February, 1896 (Kew).
78. Letter to Miss Gleeson, 31 March, 1896.
79. Letter to Miss Gleeson, 13 April, 1896.
80. Letter to Miss Gleeson, 31 March, 1896.
81. Letter to Miss Gleeson, 11 May, 1896.
82. *Ibid.*
83. Letter to Miss Gleeson, 12 June, 1896.
84. Letter to Miss Gleeson, 23 June, 1896.
85. Letter to Miss Gleeson, 27 June, 1896.
86. Letter to Miss Gleeson, 14 November, 1896.
87. Letter to Sargent, 13 January, 1897 (Arnold Arboretum).
88. Letter to Thistleton-Dyer, 14 July, 1896 (Kew).
89. Letter to Miss Gleeson, 1 May, 1897.
90. Letter to Miss Gleeson, 29 June, 1897.
91. Letter to Miss Gleeson, 29 August, 1896.
92. See letter to Thistleton-Dyer, 30 April, 1897 (Kew).
93. Letter to Miss Gleeson, 28 January, 1897.
94. *Ibid.*
95. Letter to Miss Gleeson, 18 February, 1897.
96. Letter to Miss Gleeson, 14 November, 1896.
97. *Ibid.*
98. Letter to Miss Gleeson, 30 June, 1898.
99. *Ibid.*
100. Letter to Miss Gleeson, 25 May, 1897.

101. Letter to Miss Gleeson, 1 May, 1899.
102. Letter to Miss Gleeson, 20 November, 1897.
103. *Ibid.*
104. Letter to Miss Gleeson, 22 September, 1896.
105. Letter to Miss Gleeson, n.d.
106. Letter to Miss Gleeson, 29 June, 1897.
107. *Ibid.*
108. Letter to Miss Gleeson, 13 September, 1898.

CHAPTER 8

109. Letter to Miss Gleeson, 19 February, 1898.
110. Letter to Thistleton-Dyer, 8 June, 1898, reprinted in *Kew Bulletin*, No. 143, 1898.
111. *Ibid.*
112. Letter to Miss Gleeson, 19 February, 1898.
113. *Ibid.*
114. *Ibid.*
115. *Ibid.*
116. *Ibid.*
117. Letter to Miss Gleeson, 30 May, 1898.
118. *Ibid.*
119. Letter to Miss Gleeson, 2 April, 1898.
120. Letter to Miss Gleeson, 19 February, 1898.
121. Letter to Miss Gleeson, 30 June, 1898.
122. *Ibid.*
123. Letter to Miss Gleeson, n.d.
124. Letter to Miss Gleeson, 8 February, 1899.
125. *Ibid.*
126. Letter to Miss Gleeson, 25 May, 1897.
127. Letter to Miss Gleeson, 8 February, 1899.
128. Letter to Thistleton-Dyer, 19 January, 1898.
129. Letter to Miss Gleeson, 10 July, 1898.
130. Letter to Miss Gleeson, 30 May, 1898.
131. *Kew Bulletin*, No. 143, 1898. Reprint of letter to Thistleton-Dyer, 8 June, 1898.
132. "Lolo" is a nickname. They are more properly termed "Yi".
133. British Museum Department of Oriental Printed Books and Manuscripts, Numbers OR. 6911–40.

P

134. *Kew Bulletin*, Nos. 147 and 148, 1899.
135. Letter to Miss Gleeson, 19 February, 1898.
136. Henry's translation. See his paper in the *Journal of the Royal Anthropological Institute*, 1903, Vol. 33.
137. Letter to Miss Gleeson, 30 May, 1898.
138. Letter to Thistleton-Dyer, 8 June, 1898, part of which appeared in *Kew Bulletin*, No. 143, 1898.
139. *Ibid.*
140. Letter to Sargent, 21 July, 1899 (Arnold Arboretum).

CHAPTER 9

141. Letter to Miss Gleeson, 1 May, 1899.
142. *Ibid.*
143. Letter to Miss Gleeson, 21 December, 1898.
144. Hermann Christ: *"Fougères de Mengtze"*, *Bulletin de l'Herbier Boissier* 6, 1898.
145. Letter to Miss Gleeson, 1 May, 1899.
146. Letter to Sargent, 9 May, 1899.
147. Letter to Sargent, 14 November, 1899.
148. *Ibid.*
149. Letter to Miss Gleeson, 1 May, 1899.
150. Letter to Miss Gleeson, 17 July, 1899.
151. *Ibid.*
152. Letter to Sargent, 8 July, 1899 (Arnold Arboretum).
153. Letter to Miss Gleeson, 20 May, 1899.
154. Letter to Miss Gleeson, 1 May, 1899.
155. Letter to Sargent, 21 July, 1899 (Arnold Arboretum).
156. Letter to Miss Gleeson, 18 September, 1899.
157. Letter to Miss Gleeson, 31 July, 1899.
158. *Ibid.*
159. Letter to Miss Gleeson, 17 July, 1899.
160. Letter to Miss Gleeson, 31 July, 1899.
161. Letter to Miss Gleeson, 6 March, 1900.

CHAPTER 10

162. Letter to Miss Gleeson, 30 June, 1898.
163. Letter to Miss Gleeson, 11 December, 1899.

164. Letter to Sargent, 14 November, 1899 (Arnold Arboretum).

165. Letter to Miss Gleeson, 5 June, 1900.

166. Letter to Miss Gleeson, 24 June, 1900.

167. Letter to Miss Gleeson, 29 June, 1900.

168. Letter to Miss Gleeson, 10 July, 1900.

169. Letter to Miss Gleeson, 16 September, 1900.

170. See J. A. Spender: *Great Britain, Empire and Commonwealth* 1886–1935.

171. Letter to Sargent, 28 November, 1901 (Arnold Arboretum).

172. See *The Times*, 12 July, 1954. I am indebted for this reference to Mr. G. R. G. Worcester, author of *The Junkman Smiles*, who is himself an ex-official of the Chinese Customs.

173. Letter to Miss Gleeson, 8 December, 1900.

CHAPTER 11

174. Letter to Miss Gleeson, 11 May, 1900.

175. Letter to Miss Gleeson, 18 March, 1901.

176. Letter to Miss Gleeson, 26 March, 1901.

177. Letter to Miss Gleeson, 5 March, 1901. See also letter to Thistleton-Dyer, Kew (Vol. 152, Japanese, Chinese and Siberian letters).

178. Letter to Miss Gleeson, 18 March, 1901.

179. Letter to Miss Gleeson, 18 June, 1901.

180. Letter to Miss Gleeson, 12 June, 1901.

181. Letter to Miss Gleeson postmarked 15 June, 1901.

182. Letter to Miss Gleeson, 17 June, 1901.

183. See letter to Miss Gleeson, 25 June, 1901.

184. Letter to Miss Gleeson, 17 June, 1901.

185. Letter to Miss Gleeson, 18 June, 1901 (2).

186. Letter to Miss Gleeson, 17 June, 1901.

187. *Ibid.*

188. *Ibid.*

189. Letter to Miss Gleeson, 24 June, 1901.

190. Letter to Miss Gleeson, 18 June, 1901 (1).

191. Letter to Miss Gleeson, 3 July, 1901.

192. *Ibid.*

CHAPTER 12

193. Letter to Miss Gleeson, 26 August, 1901.
194. *Ibid.*
195. Letter to Miss Gleeson, 3 February, 1900.
196. Letter to Miss Gleeson, 22 August, 1901.
197. Letter to Miss Gleeson, 2 September, 1901.
198. Letter to Miss Gleeson, 26 August, 1901.
199. *Ibid.*
200. *Ibid.*
201. *Ibid.*
202. *Ibid.*
203. Letter to Miss Gleeson, 2 September, 1901.
204. Letter to Miss Gleeson, 9 September, 1901.
205. *Ibid.*
206. Letter to Miss Gleeson, 15 September, 1901.
207. Letter to Miss Gleeson, 23 September, 1901.
208. *Ibid.*
209. Letter to Miss Gleeson, 10 December, 1901 (postmark).
210. Letter to Miss Gleeson, 19 October, 1901.
211. Letter to Miss Gleeson, 23 September, 1901.
212. *Ibid.*
213. *Ibid.*
214. *Ibid.*
215. *Ibid.*
216. *Ibid.*
217. H. J. Elwes: *Memoirs of Travel, Sport and Natural History.*
218. *Ibid.*
219. *Ibid.*
220. *Gardeners' Chronicle*, 12 April, 1902.
221. Letter to Miss Gleeson, 9 April, 1902.
222. *Gardeners' Chronicle*, 12 April, 1902.
223. *Ibid.*

CHAPTER 13

224. See Henry's evidence before the Departmental Committee in the *Report to the Department of Agriculture*, 1908.
225. *The Times*, 31 March, 1902, summarised in *Gardeners' Chronicle*, 12 April, 1902.

226. Letter to Miss Gleeson, 30 April, 1902.
227. Letter to Miss Gleeson, 27 March, 1902.
228. Letter to Miss Gleeson, 14 May, 1902.
229. *Ibid.*
230. Letter to Miss Gleeson, 20 May, 1902.
231. *Ibid.*
232. *Ibid.*
233. *Ibid.*
234. Letter to Miss Gleeson, 20 July, 1902.
235. Letter to Miss Gleeson, 26 July, 1902. The reference was to John XX, 27. Henry telegraphed this on 26 July and followed it with a letter.
236. *Ibid.*
237. Letter to Miss Gleeson, 31 July, 1902.
238. This is summarised in the British Association Proceedings and printed in the *Journal of the Royal Anthropological Institute*, 1903, Vol. 33. See Note 136 on page 226.

CHAPTER 14

239. Letter to Miss Gleeson, 12 October, 1902.
240. Letter to Miss Gleeson, 3 November, 1902.
241. Letter to Miss Gleeson, 26 October, 1902.
242. Letter to Miss Gleeson, 15 October, 1902 (postmark).
243. Letter to Miss Gleeson, 3 November, 1902.
244. Letter to Miss Gleeson, 10 December, 1901 (postmark).
245. Letter to Miss Gleeson, 13 October, 1902.
246. Letter to Miss Gleeson, 26 October, 1902.
247. *Ibid.*
248. Letter to Miss Gleeson, 13 December, 1902.
249. Lecture, "Forests, Wild and Cultivated", *Economic Proceedings of Royal Dublin Society, Vol. 1, Part 5,* October, 1904.
250. See *Report to the Department of Agriculture*, 1908 (see Note 224 on page 228), Appendix.
251. Letter to Miss Gleeson, 13 December, 1902. The sentence was in the current number of *The Garden.* Henry had contributed an article on *Lilium henryi* to the October 25 number.
252. Letter to Miss Gleeson, 29 January, 1903.

253. Letter to Miss Gleeson, 18 December, 1902.
254. Letter to Miss Gleeson, 27 November, 1902.
255. Quoted in letter to Miss Gleeson, 14 November, 1902.
256. Letter to Miss Gleeson, 9 March, 1903.
257. Letter to Thistleton-Dyer, 7 April, 1903 (Kew).
258. *Ibid.*
259. Letter to Thistleton-Dyer, 13 April, 1903 (Kew).
260. *Ibid.*
261. Letter to Miss Gleeson, 19 May, 1903.
262. *Ibid.*
263. Letter to Miss Gleeson, 28 June, 1903.
264. As mentioned in letter to Miss Gleeson, 3 April, 1903.
265. Letter to Miss Gleeson, 15 July, 1903.
266. *Ibid.*
267. *Ibid.*
268. *Ibid.*
269. *Ibid.*
270. *Ibid.*
271. Lecture, "Forests, Wild and Cultivated", *Economic Proceedings of Royal Dublin Society, Vol. 1, Part 5*, October, 1904.

CHAPTER 15

272. *Cheltenham Chronicle*, 17 May, 1958.
273. *Revue des Eaux et Forêts*, Vol. 53, January, 1914. *"Leur ouvrage est un des plus utiles . . . qui aient été publiés sur les arbres croissants non pas seulement dans la Grande Bretagne et Irlande mais dans la plus grande partie de l'Europe où se rencontrent les mêmes espèces."* L. Pardé.
274. H. J. Elwes: *Memoirs of Travel, Sport and Natural History* (from papers collected after his death), published by Ernest Benn.
275. See letter to Miss Gleeson, 8 August, 1903, and also letter to C. F. Millspaugh, 12 January, 1923, in the Natural History Museum, Chicago.
276. Letter to Miss Gleeson, 8 August, 1903.
277. Letter to Miss Gleeson, 21 September, 1903.
278. Letter to Miss Gleeson, 18 September, 1903.
279. Letter to Miss Gleeson, 21 February, 1905.

280. Letter to Miss Gleeson, 24 August, 1904.
281. Letter to Miss Gleeson, 23 December, 1904.
282. Letter to Miss Gleeson, 20 October, 1904.
283. Letter to Miss Gleeson, 16 January, 1905. See also Proceedings of Linnean Society 1904–5 for abstract of Henry's discourse on *Botanical Collecting*.
284. Letter to Miss Gleeson, 2 October, 1905.
285. Letter to Miss Gleeson, 14 September, 1905.
286. Letter to Miss Gleeson, 18 April, 1906.
287. Letter to Miss Gleeson, 20 October, 1905.

CHAPTER 16

288. Letter to Miss Gleeson, 21 June, 1901.
289. Letter to Miss Gleeson, 28 October, 1902.
290. *Ibid.*
291. Notebooks of Mrs. Alice Henry in the National Library of Ireland.
292. I am indebted for this remark of Mrs. Henry's to her friend Miss Sylvia Fannin.
293. Letter to Miss Gleeson, 10 May, 1906.
294. Letter to Miss Gleeson, 10 July, 1906.
295. Letter to Colonel Prain (later Sir David Prain), 25 September, 1906 (Kew).
296. Letter to Colonel Prain, 11 October, 1906 (Kew).
297. Letter to Colonel Prain, 25 September, 1906 (Kew).
298. Letter to Colonel Prain (Kew).
299. Letter to Miss Gleeson, 28 February, 1907.
300. Letter to Miss Gleeson, 12 March, 1907.
301. *Ibid.*
302. Letter to Miss Gleeson, 15 March, 1907.
303. Letter to Miss Gleeson, 26 March, 1907.
304. See *Quarterly Journal of Forestry*, 1907.
305. *Journal of the Royal Horticultural Society*, LXVII, p. 385.
306. Letter to Miss Gleeson, 14 September, 1907.
307. See his evidence in the *Report to the Department of Agriculture*, 1908.
308. *Ibid.*
309. *Ibid.*
310. Letter to Miss Gleeson, 25 December, 1907.

311. Letter to Miss Gleeson, 20 April, 1908.
312. Diary of Anne Brunton in the National Library of Ireland.

CHAPTER 17

313. Letter to Miss Gleeson.
314. Letter to Miss Gleeson, 17 November, 1908.
315. Quoted by her sister, Mrs. Kruming (Anne Brunton), in a letter to author.
316. Letter to Miss Gleeson, 9 July, 1908.
317. Letter to Miss Gleeson, 17 November, 1908.
318. Letter to Miss Gleeson, 5 August, 1908.
319. Letter to Miss Gleeson, 12 January, 1910 (dated 1909 by Henry, evidently a slip).
320. W. B. Yeats: *The Man and the Echo, Last Poems*, 1936–39. Robert Brennan, one of the leaders of the 1916 rebellion, who was sentenced to death but reprieved, writes in his memoirs:
    "The effect of the play on the young men and women of the Gaelic League and Sinn Fein was profound . . . To the question which Yeats asked thirty-six years later:
    Did that play of mine send out
    Certain men the English shot?
    I can without hesitation answer 'Yes'."
    See Robert Brennan: *Allegiance*, 1950.
321. Letter to Miss Gleeson, 5 August, 1908.
322. Letter to Miss Gleeson, 17 November, 1908.
323. Letter to Miss Gleeson, 19 December, 1909.
324. Letter to Miss Gleeson, 5 August, 1908.
325. I am indebted to Mrs. Kruming for a number of anecdotes and personal reminiscences, conveyed in notes which I have returned to her.
326. Sir Frederick Moore, *Journal of the Royal Horticultural Society*, LXVII, p. 385.
327. Griffith's *The Resurrection of Hungary: a parallel for Ireland* had appeared in 1904. See also *Sinn Fein*, Nos. 1 and 6, 1906.
328. Letter to Miss Gleeson, 5 September, 1909.
329. Letter to Miss Gleeson, 17 November, 1908.
330. Letter to Miss Gleeson, 19 December, 1909.

331. Printed in *The Week-end Book*, 1924.

332. Letter to Miss Gleeson, 11 June, 1910.

333. Letter to Miss Gleeson, 19 December, 1909.

334. A. Henry: *On elm seedlings showing Mendelian results.* Journal Linnean Soc. of London (Bot. 39), 1910.

335. "Poplars can be Bred to Order," by Ernst J. Schreiner, *U.S. Dept. of Agriculture Yearbook*, 1949. See also *Journal of New York Botanic Garden*, March, 1927: "The Breeding of Forest Trees for Pulp Wood," by Stout, McKee and Schreiner, in which Henry's paper is quoted.

336. Letter to Miss Gleeson, 2 August, 1911.

337. H. J. Elwes: *Memoirs of Travel, Sport and Natural History* (from papers collected after his death), published by Ernest Benn.

338. Letter to Miss Gleeson, 23 January, 1911.

339. Letter to Miss Gleeson, 6 December, 1904.

340. Letter to Miss Gleeson, 19 January, 1913.

CHAPTER 18

341. Notebooks of Mrs. Alice Henry in the National Library of Ireland, MS 7981–7.

342. "Ireland and the German Menace," *Irish Review*, September, 1912. "Ireland, Germany and the Next War," *Irish Review*, July, 1913. "From Coffin Ship to Atlantic Greyhound," *Irish Review*, February, March and April, 1914.

343. "I saw no evidence of mental derangement when I examined him but I thought he had some lesion in his brain as his tongue was protruded to the left." Letter to Mrs. Alice Henry, 6 May, 1916. Original in notebooks of Mrs. Alice Henry in the National Library of Ireland.

344. Memoir in typescript by the late Miss E. Stopford.

345. Quoted in Diary of Anne Brunton in the National Library of Ireland.

346. Notebooks of Mrs. Alice Henry.

347. *Ibid.*

348. *Ibid.*

349. *Ibid.*

350. *Ibid.*

351. Original pasted in notebooks of Mrs. Alice Henry.
352. Original pasted in notebooks of Mrs. Alice Henry.
353. *An Claidheamh Soluis*, the official organ of the Gaelic League. The article "The North Began" appeared on 1 November, 1913. See "The Volunteers", by Bulmer Hobson, *Irish Times*, 19 November, 1963.
354. Notebooks of Mrs. Alice Henry.
355. *Ibid.*
356. "The Volunteers," by Bulmer Hobson, *Irish Times*, 19 November, 1963.
357. *Irish Times*, 2 February, 1914; "From Coffin Ship to Atlantic Greyhound," *Irish Review*, February, 1914.
358. Notebooks of Mrs. Alice Henry.
359. According to his own account in the *Irish Times*, 25 July, 1964.
360. Notebooks of Mrs. Alice Henry.
361. *Ibid.*
362. Original pasted in notebooks of Mrs. Alice Henry.

CHAPTER 19

363. Notebooks of Mrs. Alice Henry in the National Library of Ireland, MS 7981–7.
364. *Ibid.*
365. *Ibid.*
366. *Ibid.*
367. *Ibid.*
368. Original in notebooks of Mrs. Alice Henry.
369. See Note 343 on page 233.
370. Constable, 1919.
371. I have not been able to find a copy of this lecture but there is a full summary in Mrs. Henry's notebooks.
372. Notebooks of Mrs. Alice Henry.
373. Copy in notebooks of Mrs. Alice Henry.
374. Original in notebooks of Mrs. Alice Henry.
375. I am indebted to Mrs. Kruming (Miss Anne Brunton) for this quotation.
376. Notebooks of Mrs. Alice Henry.

377. "The History of the London Plane," "The History of the Dunkeld Hybrid Larch," "The Douglas Firs," in collaboration with Miss M. G. Flood: *Proceedings of the Royal Irish Academy*, *35*, Sections A and B, 1919–20.

378. *Cummann Leigheacht an Phobail Publications 1921*, in National Library of Ireland.

379. Letter in possession of Mrs. Kruming.

380. "Co-operation of Citizen and State in Forestry," *Studies*, December, 1924.

381. Letter to Miss Gleeson, 3 August, 1927.

382. Robert Browning: *A Grammarian's Funeral*.

383. Letter to Miss Gleeson, 24 December, 1928.

APPENDIX I

Short List of Plants Discovered by Augustine Henry

There is no complete list of plants discovered by Augustine Henry. The names of most of them are to be found scattered through the *Index Florae Sinensis*, the long catalogue referred to in Chapter 3. This was begun by a committee in 1886, taken over by the Linnean Society in the 1890s and carried on by it till 1905. A list of about three hundred is given by Dr. E. Bretschneider in his *History of European Botanical Discoveries in China*, published in 1898. Other sources of information are J. G. Baker's *New Ferns*, 1892, his papers on ferns in the *Journal of Botany* between 1887 and 1889, and a paper on *"Fougères de Mengtze"* by Hermann Christ in the *Bulletin de l'Herbier Boissier* 6, 1898.

The total of numbered specimens that Henry sent to Kew is as follows:

From	Hupeh and Sze-Chwan	8,161
	Hainan Island	839
	Yunnan	4,800
	Odd places in China	90
	Formosa	2,090
		15,980

Duplicates of most of these were purchased by Harvard. Sets from Mengtze went to Calcutta, St. Petersburg, Missouri, Edinburgh, Hong-Kong and St. Louis, and possibly other herbaria too. Incidentally, the price he quotes in a letter to Professor Sargent (25 December, 1901, Arnold Arboretum) is only fifty shillings a hundred sheets.

The greatest number of novelties were contained in the first collections sent from I-chang and the fruits of the two journeys through Hupeh and Sze-Chwan. These included 20 new genera and 500 new species. The total number of new genera discovered by him varies from 25 to 30 in different accounts. The discrepancies may be due to problems of classification. Some of Henry's specimens have never been botanically described.

Garden Plants

From the general reader's point of view, it is disappointing to have to admit that out of all this large number of plants only a few dozen have any garden merit. Henry himself had never been a gardener, and he was not working for commercial nurseries. But he did make a few real horticultural "finds", and Wilson and Forrest, who were sent out after him to look for garden plants, discovered far more. With them began the great spate of horticultural introductions.

While working on this biography I have naturally been on the look out for plants associated with Henry's name. As an amateur gardener I have compiled my own short list, assisted by current catalogues, and I hope it may interest other gardeners, though I cannot claim that it is complete. Everything on it may fairly be attributed to Henry, though a few plants had actually been discovered earlier by collectors from other countries like Father David. In most cases what Henry sent home were specimens, and the actual introduction of the plants must be credited to E. H. Wilson or George Forrest.

The letters A.M., A.G.M. and F.C.C. refer to the Royal Horticultural Society's Award of Merit, Award of Garden Merit, and First Class Certificate.

TREES

Acer henryi. This is recommended by Bean in his *Ornamental Trees for Amateurs*, 1925, for its autumn colour and ornamental fruit. It seems to have dropped out of the lists. I have seen one at Mount Usher, Co. Wicklow, but this is an out of the ordinary garden. I suspect it may not be very hardy.
Acer nikoense. I have not identified this (there is a bewildering number of maples) but Hillier's catalogue says it is "very hardy and beautiful".

Acer oliverianum. This is also recommended by Hillier's.

Cercis racemosa. A.M. 1927. A beautiful relation of the beautiful "Judas tree".

Davidia involucrata (see Chapter 3). I have seen many fine specimens.

Eucommia ulmoides. The only tree hardy in a temperate climate that produces rubber. You can see the rubbery substance when you tear a leaf. This is the "gutta percha" tree that Henry found growing in County Kerry (see Chapter 16). There is one also at Mount Usher. It is quite ornamental. The rubber is not of economic use—you can't grow your own tyres!

Gymnocladus chinensis. This is not hardy. I include it because, as with the "Tulip trees", there are only two species and the other is North American. *Gymnocladus dioicus (canadensis)* is recommended in the last (1956) edition of Robinson's *English Flower Garden.*

Ilex macrocarpa. Robinson's *English Flower Garden* (1956 edition) describes this as "a vigorous deciduous tree with black fruits". In Hillier's 1963-4 list it is unpriced, which means not at present available.

Liriodendron chinense. The Chinese "tulip tree". The North American *Liriodendron tulipifera* is hardier. There are specimens of both at Mount Usher. They are much alike. The flowers are to my mind disappointing and not at all like tulips, but the leaves are handsome and turn clear yellow in autumn.

Poliothyrsis sinensis. A.M. 1960. I do not know this, and it is unpriced in Hillier's 1963-4 list. It is described as a small tree or large shrub with cream-coloured panicles in July.

SHRUBS

Buddleia davidii. A.M. 1898. This is the common old purple buddleia, parent of some excellent varieties.

Cotoneaster henryanus. A.M. 1920. Evergreen, about twelve feet high, with long leaves and red berries. There is one growing against a wall in the Irish National Botanic Gardens at Glasnevin, but it is not necessarily a wall shrub. That great landscape gardener, Mr. Russell Page, in his *Education of a Gardener,* 1962, mentions this as one of the "more aristocratic" cotoneasters.

Deutzia discolor. A well-known deutzia with many good forms.

Hypericum patulum henryi. A.M. 1904, A.G.M. 1924. Henry's variety of this well-known hypericum was the first with large flowers. It has been superseded by finer ones, such as "Hidcote" and "Rowallane Hybrid".

Itea ilicifolia. A handsome evergreen with long greenish-white racemes, good in shade. Perhaps more in Victorian than contemporary taste.

Lonicera pileata. A.M. 1910. In an article on Henry's plants in the *Gardeners' Chronicle,* 9 November, 1935, J. W. Besant says this is a better hedge plant than *L. nitida.*

Rhododendron augustinii. One of Henry's most important discoveries. A.G.M. 1924, A.M. 1926. Blue or grey-blue flowered. Parent of many blue hybrids.

Rhododendron auriculatum. A.M. 1922. Also a valuable rhododendron, remarkable for flowering late, in August. Large white scented flowers.

Spiraea henryi. A.M. 1934. I do not know this spiraea, but Hillier's say it is of first-class merit.

Staphylea holocarpa. A.M. 1924. A "bladder nut" with white flowers and curious seed vessels. More a small tree than a shrub.

Sycopsis sinensis. A.M. 1926. I do not know this either. It belongs to the "Witch Hazel" family.

Viburnum henryi. F.C.C. 1910, awarded for its beauty in fruit. It is a bushy viburnum with shiny long leaves. I have only seen a poor specimen.

Viburnum rhytidophyllum. F.C.C. 1907. There is a fine one in the garden of the Henrys' house at Sandford Terrace. This is a shrub of character with a branching growth and large handsome leaves. It bears clusters of red berries turning black, but Hillier's say single specimens do not fruit freely. I am pleased to find my liking for it endorsed by Mr. Russell Page in his book quoted on page 239.

CLIMBERS

Actinidia chinensis. A.M. 1907. First seen by Fortune, rediscovered by Henry. Handsome parti-coloured leaves. The fruits are said to be edible.

Actinidia henryi. This form is less colourful and less hardy. Both are growing at Mount Usher, and *chinensis* is certainly the one to recommend.

Celastrus angulata (latifolius). I do not know this. Robinson's *English Flower Garden* (1956) says it is a rampant deciduous shrub which may be used to clothe a wall.

Clematis henryi. A variety of the Lanuginosa type, with large white flowers and dark stamens.

Decumaria sinensis. I do not know this. *The English Flower Garden* says it is a beautiful hardy species "found by Dr. Henry covering the cliffs of the I-chang Gorge with clusters of fragrant white flowers."

Lonicera henryi. A useful evergreen for clothing a wall.

Parthenocissus henryana. (*Vitis henryana*, "the Henry vine"). A.M. 1906, A.G.M. 1936. A vigorous self-clinging creeper with prettily veined leaves. Excellent for covering a wall in shade. Deciduous.

Schizophragma integrifolia. A.M. 1936, F.C.C. 1963. I do not know this but there is a striking illustration of it in the 1956 edition of *The English Flower Garden*. Hillier's say it resembles the climbing hydrangea in growth but is more conspicuous in flower. It likes sun.

LILIES AND OTHER PLANTS

Lilium henryi. (See Chapter 3.) A tall, lime-loving lily with loose heads of deep yellow reflexing flowers.

Henry also discovered two new varieties of *Lilium brownii.* His collections threw fresh light on the distribution of several other lilies such as *L. giganteum, L. nepalense, L. pumilum, L. tigrinum,* and *L. willmottiae.*

Corydalis thalictrifolia. "A charming addition to rock garden plants" (*The English Flower Garden*).

Lysimachia henryi. I remember this creeping yellow-flowered plant in a garden that has now gone. I could not find it in any list but that of the Daisy Hill Nurseries, Newry.

Rehmannia angulata. A showy half-hardy biennial. It was a favourite of Henry's. In a letter to Evelyn Gleeson of 15 April, 1906, he speaks of his pride in seeing a bed of it at Wisley.

Arundinaria nitida. The well-known bamboo.

APPENDIX 2

Publications of Augustine Henry

The Trees of Great Britain and Ireland (in collaboration with H. J. Elwes), 7 Volumes, 1906–13. Privately printed.
Forests, Woods and Trees in relation to Hygiene (three Chadwick Lectures), Constable, 1919.
Notes on the Economic Botany of China, Presbyterian Mission Press, Shanghai, 1893.
A List of Plants from Formosa, supplement to *Transactions of the Japanese Asiatic Society 24*, 1896. See also *Kew Bulletin*, Nos. 111 and 112, 1896.

ARTICLES AND PAPERS
Chinese Names of Plants, *China Royal Asiatic Society Journal*, *22*, 1887.
Vegetable Productions of Central China, *Kew Bulletin*, 1889.
Notes on Two Mountain Antelopes of Central China, *Zoological Society Proceedings*, 1890.
Chinese Jute, China—Imperial Maritime Customs 11. Special series No. 16, Shanghai.
Memorandum on the Jute and Hemp of China, *Kew Bulletin*, 1891.
Shu-lang root (Dioscorea rhipogonoides, Oliver), *Kew Bulletin*, 1895.
Chinese Soap Trees, *The American Druggist*, 1896.
Botany of Formosa, *Kew Bulletin*, 1897.
Botanical Explorations in Yunnan, *Kew Bulletin*, 1897.
A Budget from Yunnan, *Kew Bulletin*, 1897, 1898, 1899 and *Garden and Forest*, 1896.
Notes from South West China, *Garden and Forest*, *10*, 1897.
Camphor, *Pharmaceutical Journal*, London, 1897.
Some exports of South China and Indo-China: Laos Cinnamon, Annam Cassia, Cardamoms, Dye-Yam, Camphor, Star Anise, *Pharmaceutical Journal*, 1898.

Castaneas, *New York Botanic Gardens Journal*, 1902.
Chinese Drugs and Medicinal Plants (Lecture to Pharmaceutical Society), *Pharmaceutical Journal*, 1902.
The Lolos and other tribes of Western China (paper read to British Association 1902), *Journal of the Anthropological Institute of Great Britain and Ireland*, 1903.
Chinese Firs (Keteleeria), *Gardeners' Chronicle*, 1903.
Some new Trees and Shrubs of Western China, *Flora and Sylva*, Vol. I, 1903.
The Chinese Tree: Cupressus Hodginsii, *Gardeners' Chronicle*, 1904.
Botanical Collecting (Abstract of discourse), *Linnean Society Proceedings*, 1904–5.
Forests, wild and cultivated. (Lecture), *Economic Proceedings of Royal Dublin Society*, Vol. I, Part 5, October, 1904.
National Importance of Forestry, *Journal of Department of Agriculture*, Ireland, 1905.
Primitive Folk in China. (Lecture), Royal Dublin Society, 1906.
Series on Forestry in *Journal of Department of Agriculture*, Ireland, 1906–7:

1. The Planting of Waste Land.
2. The Proper Methods of Planting Forest Trees.
3. Trees for Poles and Timber.
4. Trees for Shelter and Ornament.
5. Planting, Management and Preservation of Shelter-Belts and Hedgerow Timber.
6. The Management of Plantations.
7. Felling and Selling of Timber.
8. The Planting and Management of Hedges.

Position of Larch in Irish Forestry, *Journal of Department of Agriculture*, Ireland, 1907.
Tree growth on Bog Land, *Journal of Department of Agriculture*, Ireland, 1910.
On elm seedlings showing Mendelian results, *Journal Linnean Society of London*, (Bot. 39), 1910.
The Giant Cypress of Formosa, *Gardeners' Chronicle*, 1912.
Woods and Trees of Ireland. (Lecture), *County Louth Archaeological Journal*, Vol. 3, 1912–15 (Abstract in *Nature*, February, 1915).

Profitable Trees, *Journal of Department of Agriculture*, Ireland, 1913.
Artificial Production of Vigorous Trees, *Journal of Department of Agriculture*, Ireland, 1914 (Abstract in *Nature*, January, 1915).
Black Poplars, *Gardeners' Chronicle*, 1914.
A New Hybrid Poplar, *Gardeners' Chronicle*, 1914.
A Hybrid Larch, *Gardeners' Chronicle*, 1915.
A new species of larch, *Transactions Royal Scottish Arboricultural Society*, 1915.
Larix pendula, *Gardeners' Chronicle*, 1915.
North American Forest Trees in Britain, *Gardeners' Chronicle*, 1915.
Cedars of Lebanon, *Country Life*, 1915, reprinted *Science American Supplement*, 1919, and *Gardeners' Chronicle*, 1923.
Afforestation of peat bogs and sand dunes, *Country Life*, 1916.
New Balsam Poplars, *Gardeners' Chronicle*, 1916.
Black Poplars, *Transactions of Royal Scottish Arboricultural Society*, Vol. XXX, 1916.
American sycamores are possibly hybrids, *Journal Heredity*, 8, U.S.A., 1917.
Fastigiate Scots Pine, *Irish Gardening*, 1918.
The History of the London Plane (in collaboration with Miss M. G. Flood), *Proceedings of the Royal Irish Academy*, 1919, (Abstract in *Nature*, June, 1919).
The History of the Dunkeld Hybrid Larch (in collaboration with Miss M. G. Flood), *Proceedings of Royal Irish Academy*, 1919, (Abstract in *Nature*, July, 1919).
The Douglas Firs (in collaboration with Miss M. G. Flood), *Proceedings of the Royal Irish Academy*, 1920 (Abstract in *Nature*, February, 1920).
Cultivation of Eucalypti, *Irish Gardening*, 1921.
Irish Forestry (pamphlet in series of *Cummann Leigheacht an Phobail Publications*, 1921. Abstract in *Quarterly Journal of Forestry*, 1923).
The Dublin Arboricultural Society, *Gardeners' Chronicle*, 1921.
The Western Larch in Cultivation, *Quarterly Journal of Forestry*, 1922, Vol. XVI, p. 161.
Obituary notice on Henry John Elwes, *Proceedings of the Royal Society*, London, 1923.
Manna of larch and of Douglas fir, Melezitose and lethal honey;

larch agaric, *Pharmaceutical Journal and Pharmacist*, 1924 (Abstract in *Nature*, April, 1924).

Co-operation of Citizen and State in Forestry, *Studies*, December, 1924.

The Swamp Cypresses, Glyptostrobus of China and Taxodium of America (in collaboration with Mrs. M. McIntyre), *Proceedings of the Royal Irish Academy*, 1926 (Abstract in *Nature*, July, 1926).

Plants and People of South-West China (Review of *Naturbilder aus Südwest-China* by Heinrich Handel-Mazzetti), *Nature*, May, 1927.

Obituary notice of Charles Sprague Sargent, *Quarterly Journal of Forestry*, 1927, Vol. XXI, p. 176.

BOOK LIST

The Dictionary of National Biography.
The Dictionary of American Biography.
Who's Who and *Who Was Who.*
Cambridge Modern History.
Encyclopaedia Britannica, edition of 1875.
W. Robinson: *The English Flower Garden,* third edition (1893) and sixteenth edition, revised by Roy Hay, 1956.
W. J. Bean: *Trees and Shrubs Hardy in the British Isles,* 1914.

Part One

Hanley F. Wright: *Hart and the Chinese Customs,* 1950.
Juliet Bredon: *Life of Sir Robert Hart,* 1909.
Sir Robert Hart: *These from the Land of Sinim,* 1901.
J. O. P. Bland and E. Backhouse: *China under the Empress Dowager,* 1910.
Lien Sheng Yang: *Money and Credit in China,* 1952.
James W. Davidson: *The Island of Formosa,* 1903.
Lancelot Giles: Diary of the Boxer Riots and of the Siege of the Legations in Peking. *Christ's College Magazine (Cambridge),* Lent Term, 1901.
J. A. Spender: *Great Britain, Empire and Commonwealth 1886–1935.*
E. Bretschneider: *History of European Botanical Discoveries in China,* 1898.
E. H. M. Cox: *Plant Hunting in China,* 1945.
Miles Hadfield: *Pioneers in Gardening,* 1955; *Gardening in Britain,* 1960.
Sir John Pratt: *China and Britain,* 1945; *Expansion of Europe into the Far East,* 1946.
G. R. G. Worcester: *The Junkman Smiles,* 1959.
E. H. Wilson: *A Naturalist in Western China,* 1913.
John F. Embree and Lilian Ota Dotson: *Bibliography of the*

Peoples and Cultures of Mainland Southeast Asia, 1950.
David Crockett Graham: *Folk Religion in South West China*, 1961.
Lin Yueh-hua: *The Lolo of Lian Shan*, 1961.
Peter Goullart: *Princes of the Black Bone*, 1959.
Edward Weyer Jr.: *Primitive Peoples Today*, 1959.
Literary and Philosophical Society of Manchester: *Proceedings, 1933–6*.
Nicholas Mansergh: *Britain and Ireland* (pamphlet), 1942.
Janet Dunbar: *Mrs. G. B. S.—A Biographical Portrait of Charlotte Shaw*, 1963.

Part Two

H. J. Elwes: *Memoirs of Travel, Sport and Natural History*, 1930.
Curtis's Botanical Magazine Dedications 1827–1927.
Geoffrey Taylor: *The Victorian Flower Garden*, 1952.
Liam Miller: *The Dun Emer Press* (*The Irish Book*, Vol. 2, 3), 1963.
Alan Denson: *Letters from A.E.*, 1961; *Printed Writings by George A. Russell* (A.E.), A Bibliography, 1961.
Proceedings of the Linnean Society 1904–5 and 1929–30.
Gardeners' Chronicle: 3 August, 1901; 12 April, 1902; 15 March, 1913; 29 March, 1930.
The Ulster Liberal Unionist Association 1885–1914 (pamphlet), 1914.
Report of the Departmental Committee on Irish Forestry, 1908.
United States Department of Agriculture Yearbook, 1949.
New York Botanic Gardens Journal: March, 1927.
Royal Horticultural Society Journal, LXVII, 1942.

Part Three

P. S. O'Hegarty: *A History of Ireland under the Union*, 1952.
Dorothy Macardle: *The Irish Republic*, 1937.
Nicholas Mansergh: *Britain and Ireland*, 1942.
Rene MacColl: *Roger Casement*, 1956.
Denis Gwynn: *The Life and Death of Roger Casement*, 1930.
Herbert O. Mackey: *The Crime Against Europe, collected writings and poems of Roger Casement*, 1958.
Lennox Robinson: *Ireland's Abbey Theatre*, 1951.
A. A. Hoehling: *Edith Cavell*, 1958.

Robert Brennan: *Allegiance*, 1950.

Cathal O'Shannon: "Gathering of the Storm Clouds" (article in *Irish Times*, 17 September, 1963).

Bulmer Hobson: "The Howth Gun Running" (article in *Irish Times*, 25 July, 1964).

Irish Forestry (*Journal of Society of Irish Foresters*), Vol. VIII, 2., XIII, 1.

Forestry in Northern Ireland (pamphlet), 1962. (Belfast.)

Report of the Minister of Lands on Forestry (*Dublin*) *1961–2*.

Obituary Notices: Linnean Society Proceedings; The Times; Gardeners' Chronicle; Nature; Kew Bulletin; Irish Times.

INDEX